Penguin Books

Trixie

Wallace Graves was born in Seattle in 1922 and was educated at the University of Washington there. He worked for six years as a carpenter in Alaska, two as an English teacher in Greece, and has been teaching in the Los Angeles area since 1959. He has had other stories published in *The Kenyon Review* and other literary magazines. *Trixie* is his first novel.

Wallace Graves

Trixie

Penguin Books

Penguin Books Ltd, Harmondsworth,
Middlesex, England
Penguin Books Australia Ltd, Ringwood,
Victoria, Australia

First published in the U.S.A. 1969
Published in Great Britain by André Deutsch Ltd 1970
Published in Penguin Books 1973

Made and printed in Great Britain by
Cox & Wyman Ltd, London, Reading and Fakenham
Set in Intertype Times

To Mama

1963 Diary

November 22, Fridy

This is the wurst awful that hapen.

Somebody kill him. The president of the U.S. of A. is ded! Jack F kenedy, oh, i love that man so much that he is ded today it make me so SIK. i am crying and i cant stop crying, Lary is gone i supose home to his wife i cant blame him but i need him or sombody oh i need sombody becase they *killed* Presadent Kenedy, oh i wish i was ded to! it is nov. 22 i know that much, the year 1963 and a terrable friday oh holy jesus it is so sad, will *always* be a day the wurst of sad days i am beginning to write my life down in memery of Jack F.K. who i loved and cant think of him not here! He is assanated today it is to awful i am crying so bad i got to stop

November 23, Sataday

NEXT DAY

Lary havent come back. Woke up crying haf the night. Lary havent even called and i am so lonsome becaus the presadent bless his darling bleeding and quiet hart is no more, i loved him. On the radio he is back in Washingtown D.C. and his darling body laying oh so still in a casket of flowers, i cant stand it if only Lary would come. Jesus, Lary, come!

i shoudent be so nesessary over Lary after all he have his wife to think about and she come first so i will haf to wait preying for the sole of my frend who is no more to go to heven wich i know he will bless his loving hart.

Lucky im not hungery lary was gon bring eggs and stuff and forget, i dident want brekfast lissening to the radio was all the brekfast i coud stand. But even soles in terrable angwish needs a litle something wich if it is not love, then a litle food will help. And i am out of mony in the rush on yesterday oh, sad, it is yesterday allready but the world still crying hard.

it is not so bad. i coud be jackaline, which is worst. All her mony is all her mony is all, wich isent anything to her pore broken hart like mine is to, and only this writting down knowes besides me. That is why i am going to keep the flame going in his sweet name so i wont cry and the world will remember.

Later.

I wish lary woud show up. i have thought so much my stomache aches more then my eyes now. i peed a while back and even it smeled like coffee which is all i had since jack killed wich is nearly 24 hours now, i wonder if jackaline have managed a bite sence then? Not even cofee, i bet. The pore first lady of our cuntry who now is some one else.

Jesus! i wish Lary would come. His wife had him a long time and there icebox have food. They from the cuntry Hungery i wonder how they feel, as much as a sole born in the USA and raised like me? Lary should remember i am a crying American who have lost all thru an evil bullet. i wish he would bring some food if he love me wich he say he do and i do him but my stomache is groweling verry bad now. Peeing about all i have left to do. i went to the ladys room just now and not a sole around. Usally there is some on sataday but not even any campus cops.

evrything caled off. even the ball games. The whole campus desserted, not even the cafateria open even if i had any mony so Lary beter come or i will die.

i just gone threw the drawrs in Larys desk. i found some cigars and a part bottel of brandy wich is to burny for me so i put a litle in my cofee and will see if the smell come out in my pee to. Mabey i will have to leave, just when things was starting to go good.

Lary will miss me. i gave him what he wanted wich is love

and some body to have peeple see him talking to like he was a cocks man wich is okay with me long as he let me stay here. it is so warm and cleen here.

i am drinking some more brandy. it cuts the cofee down and makes me feel sad in a much hapier way. it is now sataday nite and stil no lary. i am going to writ a pome

Lary come and fill me with
a hamberger and choclate malted milk.
They are berrying darling Jack f. Kennedy
in swaths of golden silk.
i am alive and he is ded and
my silver tears fall on the floor
i will not eat till Lary comes and
jacks sole in heven for ever more.

The brandy tasts beter the more you drink. I woudent mind having lary here just to lay around with and he coud diddle me some, but i woud like a good big diner beter. Messages coming in from all over the world on how sowerful people are. Nobody wil come around for the rest of the nite. i am alone on my bed behind larys piano in the practise room. The campus desserted. Nobody know i am here except jack kenedys sole in heven wich know. He can look down on me, thru the brick walls of the musik bilding thru the paded walls of the practice room right here behind larys piano on my bed seeing me writ words of love to his memery. He will forgive me, whatever sins he think i have done he will know. He will take care of me tonite when lary dont show up. He will comfort my stomache. He will kiss my eyes asleep when it is time and will wake them in the morning unless during the dark he wants me, his frend Trixie Mae Smith, to come to his sweet heven wich i will, what he wants, if he wants, i am his servent and his everlasting slave my darling Jack F. Kenedy.

Later.

Dam Lary anyhow, i hope he havent gone back to Hungery wich he was kiked out of meny yeres ago by the reds. Now i have a stinky headache along with my stomache ache and i know i shoudent get mad becase Lary probly home crying like me all weekend, but i haf to go steel some tuna fish or something, excep it is now by larys clock in the next ofice midnite sataday and nobody open or care. i am geting sick of writting. Lary told me when he brung me here he woud keep me in good shape and see i got a good lerning at colege.

i tole him i been out of scool since i was 12.

He said he coud fix it up with his frends. Well, he is fixed it up. i am now living in this sound-prooved litle practise room next his office in the musik bilding. My life consist of i go to clases wich dont need no writting until i learn how, and leting Lary diddle me when he feal like it, and sence i am now 15 year of age & much older acting i mix in with the colege kids so they dont notice me. They is 7 thousand here so i am not noticed. i am warm and okay, but when i dont have no food or mony to get it with i am not okay.

i am miserable.

But who woud of thougt Friday morning a terrable litle man wich they already caugt woud of killed our presadent? Not Lary. So he left without me having nothing but his cigars, the hot plate and cofee pot and the brandy and all the pensils and paper i can eat, plus his piano wich i am not aloud to play excepting with the door closed becase of the cops and janaters and i cant stand it with the door closed becase i am so *awful* hungery.

now about 2 in the Sunday morning. Nobody on the radio is having any comercials, only spirital musik and stuff from Dalas and Washingtown D.C. Jack is laying in congress. Tonite Jacky & Bobby have went to see him again, on TV & radio. Jacky was all in black black tearful vales.

i wish texas was never invented, becase of Jack Kenedy. People there spit in peeples faces even before this. Where was the FBI when so sorely needed? Chasing spys? Oh the terible peeple who did this! They will haf to pay with there whole lives forever, in their own harts if noplace else. We got a new presadent from texas. i forgive him what i sayed about texas. it is a sorer wound for him. Lary, Lary! help! am i going to dye like some body at the south pole with onley messages froze in the snow? i gess i better leave in the morning, hating to becase i want to go to scool (colege!) but supose i woud of got caugt before i finished anyways. i cant writ anymore. i am going to drink the last brandy, take a final pee, brush my teeth and go to bed preying that heven has open its lovly golden gates and that he *He* is there now and for ever more.

November 24, Sundy

How coud it hapen! They have kill lee ozwald that litle man who started this terible weekend! How coud it, and lary still havent showed up. i herd the bullet sounds over the radio i herd them, murder on the radio & if i woud of had TV, id of seen it, jest after 9 oclock acording to Larys clock, i herd the shot & somebody holler Jack, you son of a bitch! could they be talking about my darling ded JFK? no, the man who done this deed is name jack ruby who is the son of a bitch but not near so bad as lee ozwald who is now also ded so i spose i got to forgive him, but cant. God im hungery, & now thay say the funrel will be tomorow a day of morning all over the U.S. of A. wich mean no scool & Lary wont come even then so i gess i beter leave, i can hichhike to Mama Popes, or even walk but its a long ways to walk on no food, i am so hungery i gess Lary forgot, wich you cant hardly blame him in this word of misry & murder.

later on sunday

i been lissening to the radio. Lovly Jack Kenedy ded and now lee ozwald ded. somthing awful going on in this cuntry. When will it stop? i am afrad to go out for fear the campus cops see me and shoot me to. They caugt jack ruby who did it on TV. The radio still playing spirital music with no comercials. The sad funral going to be tomorrow. if Lary dont bring food they will haf to berry me to. Oh, to be berryed with lovly jack who i love and who is now gone. i went thru larys drawers and didn't find a red cent. it been 48 hours sence i ate and my skinny ass is skinnier than it was, in my weakness i will write a pome

Salad, steak, gobs of gravy over mashed potatoes
is Lary
tuna sanwich on thik rye bred is
Lary to
Lary is melts and seven up, Lary is.
And hard boyled eggs
Mayonaise and choclate candy and warm
Mush for me.
Lary is. But jack is ded, nothing to eat.
Onley cold kisses.

November 25, Monday

Lary come at 7 p.m. last nite just when i desided to leave. i had packed my things in 2 big paper grocery sacks but scared to leve for fear the campus cops woud shoot me cause the whole cuntry is trigger happy now waiting for the next TV murder. But i had went 2 and one haf days on cofee & brandy wich is not good for you.

Lary brung some canned soup wich i can make hot in the basin, thay got awful hot water here. & he brung some Baby Ruths & bread & cheese & stuff & some ice creem wich we et rite away before it melt & he says a good way to start eating agen. He coudent stay on acount of his wife in a state of colapse over JFK & Lee Ozwold and all the terible things the reds done, she in bed, & cant wach TV no more. She wached the part where the new presadent was swore in & the plane got to Washingtown D.C. ect, & where the body of darling jack laying in the White House & then wen the part come of jacky yesterdy going to see the body at the place where they moved it from the White House, Larys wife went to pieces & hes had to stay ever sense. The onely reason he got out was to go to the store for milk, & he brung me food while out. Larys wife on pills. Mebbe she loved Jack as much as me, but i think nobody coud, but she is older & her body cant take it so good as me, his grate loss, i wish i had TV – or mabey it woud of been that much worser & i am lucky onely to have my radio. Now the funerel is on. A horse named Black Jack behind the coffin without a rider. i dont think i coud wach it on TV without being worse then Larys wife. Thats a funny name for the horse. Black Jack. JFK was trying to be good to black peeple. i wisht he been black, i woud love him even more. i hope i kin get a pichur of Black Jack from the paper tomorrow. i will save it forever, if i do.

Now it is late. i am laying proped up in bed behind the piano. i went to the can for the last time tonite. nobody on the whole campus excep me. the world is tukked into bed. Jacky is tukked in bed, sleeping all alone for a change, so are her 2 babys carolyne & litel john-john. So is Bobby with his wife & meny meny childern. So is the mama & papa of jack, somplace, tukked in bed. Mabey Woody is still up, ploting things like he is always ploting, but Mama Pope in bed. So is Lary, with his wife, probly still sobing or mabey over it by now. And Jack. Darling jack in his bed. They berryed him. Tonite on the news it say Jacky & Bobby gone to the grave to put a litle bokay of flowers. They give her the flag that been over his coffin for a Keepsake. She stumbeled on the way out, pore woman. A minister sayed something from the bible that Jack hisself often loved, where there is no vision, the people will perish. And now we have not Jack. But a flame burns eternal at his grave. Eternal rest for him, O Lord, let the lite in darling heven shine on him for us on erth, o Lord, you please here my prayr and lissen to me from the nite where everybody sleeps excep me, & maybey Woody. They sed at the hospital Jackys eyes looked like a traped animal, wich i kin well beleeve. Mr Jonson, the new one, set rite down after he got home & the very first 2 letters he writ was to litel carolyne & john-john. That was nice, but john-john onely 3. i wonder kin he reed.

November 26, Tusday

Russia sayed on the radio last nite it was the U.S. of A.s falt for JFK dying, thay sayed the peple like that Bery Golwater & peeple like him done it. Now i know why Lary left Hungery, he sayed he codent stand the reds no more. i codent ether, if they blamed Jack on me!

Nite. Scool is back in. evrybodys gone home excep the janaters & i got orders to stay away from them. Lary say if i get caught both our asses be in a sling along with Prof Boiloos (he also in on the action) & not much kin hapen to them, but i get sent back to Watts & probly threw in juvanile when they fine out about me, *& i dont want that.*

Dere Diry, i will tell you all about my life, on account of wile you was only born on nov. 22, 1963, i was born meny years before, wich i will tell you about, i was born in Febuary 12, 1948, wich make me 16 yrs old on my next birthday. I am Trixie Mae Smith. i am a girl with very prety lite skin wich Woody make fun of, say i dont have enuff color in me to count, jest enuff for mister charlie to notice. But Woodys a black muslim (*this* year, at least – he always swapping around) & he have nutty ideas. He says im color struck but im not. i just hapen to be a lot of evrything. Black Spannish, mostly. Mama Pope, she unnerstands, she says, Trixie Mae, you may have one hell of a time for a wile, Lord knows, with your black eyes & your nappy hair & that lite skin, but you jest remember, the kristal ball he say good things for your life, an when anybody ask you, you wite or black or West Indian or Chinee, you jest say American.

Thats good advice, & thats why I feel Jacks dying so hard. (Harder then Larys wife, i think, no matter what she makes out of it) Im American. Mama Pope kin tell the future, Diry. She wont tell me *everything*, but sometime she say things that come out true almost rite away, like how good Lary is for me.

Well, Dere Diry, i promise to tell you what hapened before you was born – they was the days when the brite life of Jack was with me to make things nice, & we could always think about him & his lovly Jacky & childern, when we felt blue. i will tell you first about Watts. Watts is where i lived till jest this fall wen i come here. i didnt have no mom, she died a long time ago & i lived around, you know. Mostly with my step daddy till he got cut up & dyed. Then with Mama Pope, sort of. And kind of with Woody. That is, i never catted like the boys done, sleeping out. But even if i slept lots of difrent places, i always have someplace. Now Lary. He is my lucky brake, because if Lary hadnt brung me here to the colege i never woud of started *you*, diry, & you woud still be laying someplace dark & cold waiting to get breethed to life. You see, Diry, your life come from Jacks breth wich is now stilled in immortal silence. Dont you feel his sole within your pages? When i put these words down they come from Jacks beating hart in heven. You are very preshous, diry. i love you, & i hope you going to lern to love me.

The first place i meet Lary was the Hole-a-go-go where Russel use to be bartender and Woody have a room over it where I stay a lot. Woody & Russel blood brothers. I worked in the kichen. I kin cook good. Lary used to come in the Hole-a-Go-Go to hear the musik. Lary is a song writter, i gess you call them songs, they are made up mostly on electric machines, and he tell me he use to get so fucking tired of writing electric songs that he like to come in the Hole-a-Go-Go and get his ears cleaned out & rewired. That musik there use to blow Larys mind. It was loud, for one thing, & have a lot of voice sounds & they play a lot of Motown sounds there like Quiksand, Martha and the Vandellas – and James Brown, Prisoner of Love, and John Coltrane and Little Stevie Wonder, Fingertips, and a lot of Rock like old Chuck Berry, and Sam Cook, Litel Red Rooster.

The first time I ever talk to Lary he look like he asleep in his chair tilted aginst the wall (but instead of asleep, storing up sounds) i notised him on acount of his eye-glasses twisted so that 1 black eyebrow magnafyed and the other glass agaynst his pink cheek made him look creepy like a passed out monster.

—that 1 eyd man going to fall off his chair, i told the cook.

—go wayke him up Trixie, the cook say.

i went out front and put my hand on his hand and sed, mister, when he opened his eyes and straitened his glasses he turned his hand up under mine and held it tite. i had on my new pink hip huggers and pink blous with the ruffeled neck unnerneath my black apron.

—plese set down, he sayd.

—i cant, i just dident want you to fall over.

—whats your name, he sayed. i seen you before.

—Trixie.

—My name is Lary, he sed with his hungery acsent.

Then Russel have the floor man chase me back to the kichen and chewed out the cook, but it wasnt nothing. There was a good crowd and in all the noise from the music nobody cared except i was under age for being out front in case a liquer inspecter hapened to be there. (i am writting this memery to last for ever, so will explayn. The law say nobody under 21 can be working where you dance and have liquer becase young kids sneak drinks and throw up)

Befor he went home Lary come back to the kichen and asked me some things about musik, wich he called The New Sound and we talked a wile. i hapen to know plenty about musik. my step daddy was a trumpet man and 1 reason he always not working was he play dixyland wich was ded when i was groing up onely he dident know it yet. dixyland dyed about wurld war 2, i think. he onely playd about 4 times a year, on holydays.

—what about rock and role? Lary sayd.

—thats ded to, i sayd. i knew what i liked wich was a new beat wich even elvis presly dident have or bobby darin or the Everly Bros. or Paul Anka, none of them, but i herd it all around me. Some of it in the Hole-a-go-go and Lary asked what the new beat do to me.

—i dont know, i sayd, ether your turned on or your not turned on, and the new beat turns me on, thats all.

—me to, Lary sayd, woud you be my music adviser?

By then the floorman lissening in.

—sure, i sayd, whats there in it for me?

—a colege edacation, he sayd.

The cook and the floorman laghed but it made me embarassed.

—no, im serous, Lary sayd, if she tells me about the new sounds ill tell her about the old ones. she can even come stay on the campus. i can fix her up with a pad there, & theres a frend of mine dying to do a study on sombody just like her. (That turned out to be Prof. Boiloo.)

When Lary left the floorman sayd – you beter stay away from that cat, Trixie, hes after your pussy not your ears.

—He *is* a colege perfessor, the cook sayed, he showed his ID to Russel one nite he have to writ a check.

—no shit, i sayd. Thats why i liked him i gess, he seemed safe.

—go ahead, the cook sayd, play along with him your not saving it for anybody anyhow. Just dont give it away to cheep.

—you be carful, the floorman sayd, first thing you know they sucker you into thinking you get somthing for free, then you make a fool of yourself and lose your natural sole and they toss you out on your skinny ass with nothing, no colege, no cherry and dont ekspect your old frends to treat you the same after that hapens.

—she aint got a cherry to lose, the cook sayd.

—how do *you* know? i sayd, i can do what i dam pleese about the perfesser.

—well, at least hes a real perfesser, the floorman sayd.

—go see Mama Pope, the cook sayd.

—Mama Pope dont know nothing better then me.

—Dont badmouth her or she'll give you the hex. Go see her and respeck her gray hairs, girl, she knows what to do.

—What you think? i sayd to the floorman.

—Go see her, he sayd. So I went & she sayd okay, that Lary was a lucky brake.

So that, in memery of jack F. Kenedy, is how i met lary, dere diry, 1 of the best known song writters in Hungery. it turned out he was not after my cherry after all or even my pussy becase Lary can not get a hard on. He come back to the Hole-a-go-go 1 afternoon with Prof. Boiloo before i started my shift and we had a talk. i had on my yellow dress & jest had my hare prosessed. Prof. Boiloo looked me over & sayd ok & Lary sayd – remember, i always get first dibs on her. So Lary sayd if i woud lissen to his music he wrote and wether it turned me on, he woud let me live in his practise room and feed me and get me in college. i tole him i hadent went to school sence the 6 grade. Prof. Boiloo sayd thats all the beter, for what I got in mind for you. He sayd I talked like a smart chick and besides the colege have a rule where a certain amount of kids got in without even finished high scool, thats how the athaletes got in. He sayd if i got in like a athalete, & worked like a athalete, i woudent be notised. What the hell, i thot, it beats living over the Hole-a-go-go even with Woody there somtime, so 1 sunday eggsackly 7 weeks ago Lary drove me over here in his sports car and here i am. litle did i know that 7 weeks latter jack F. Kenedy woud be ded and me alive but nerely dyed of hunger.

Naked, Lary is white as a peeled pear.

November 28, Thursday

This is thanksgiving wich is why nobody in scool & another weekend coming up alone, mebbe i can sneak down & see Woody or Mama Pope. Dere Diry, i sweared i woudent *never* miss a day talking to you, & i alredy did, yesterdy, & so much more to tell you. But was pooped out from writting. Now i have the whole weekend, so here goes. Lary gone with his wife off somewheres so she kin get over Jacks dying. The man in the car with Jack & Jacky, Governer Conerly in texas, he sayd from the hospital today, Jacky screemed when Jack got hit – Oh, my god! They killed my husband! Jack! Jack!

And Diry, *i* felt her screem those very words when it hapened. *i* felt a chill go thru me, like the chills Mama Pope say she feels when somthing hit her that hapens a long ways off. In my 10 oclock class on friday, haf-way thru, i felt it hit me so hard i yelped out & Prof. Boiloo stoped talking & loked at me. By the time class over, the halls full of it, people wispered the presadents been shot. i knowed what hit me then. People thot he wasent hurt bad at first, but i knowed where i felt it in my brayne and throte. i was rite, but i onely telling *you*, Diry, how Jacks spirit & trajedy hit me from so many miles away. Mabe i will tell Mama Pope, to.

But i was gon tell you more about colege. First, here is what i am learning, wich i will paste on the page,

Coarse		Name	Credats	Teecher
ANTHRO	150	Comparative Culturs	(3)	Prof. B
MUSIK	105	Unnderstaning Musik	(3)	Lary
MUSIK	309A	Amer. Foke Musik	(2)	Lary
ANTHRO	204	Culturel Anthro	(3)	Prof. B
P.E.	169	Danse & Rythm	(1)	Miss Lench

i am gon haf to study writting, Lary says, before i can take a writting coarse. He will give me a A in his 2 coarses and says Prof. Boiloo in ANTHRO is going give me a A to, so to get off on a good start. You have to keep your avarage up, even if you did get in like the athaletes. i think Prof. Boiloo intarested in me. ANTHRO is a coarse about things what go on today, like at Watts and the new sounds and so forth, along with studing what Prof. Boiloo says is 'pre-litarate peeple' wich is peeple who cant writ. i am not 'pre-litarate' but Lary says i am dam near wich is why Prof. Boiloo so intarested in me.

i think.

am all out of my blak-and-white creem, & pimples on my chin from eating bad last weak. Must get som.

November 29, Friday

Lary surprized me by stoping by last nite with some cold turky his wife baked. Luky thing, i jest pomaded my hare. Dixy Peech pomade smells nise. We had a tail-all-cozy, i think he calls it, wich hapens quite a bit & why Lary pays for keeping me here. As usal, after eating in his office, Lary pushed his glasses up and rubed his eyes – Time for a tail-all-cozy, he sayd. i know what that meant, it meant to make love in Hungery. We went in the practise room and i toke off my dress (was wering the blue shift) as usal, and put on my white nitey, not my baby doll on acount of the baby doll has pants. You can see clean thru the nitey, but its nylon and keeps me from geting to drafty. i laid down on my bed in the usal position, staring up at the cieling with all the litle holes in the cieling to cut the sound down. My bed is behind of the piano, wich is a very low cut piano so i look up into larys face staring down at me while he sets on the other side, compleatly naked. He has a old piano stool that you can spin up high like stools that are high, so he play the keys at just the level of his nuts, and looks down at me.

It was very nice. i like my body and so dose lary. He is a smart cat and he started making up music. The tape recorder on. i coud see just down to his sholders. Lary so harry that he has to shave his sholders to keep his body hair from showing around his shirtneck, so there was his pink face with his hair cut flat top like a brush, and them gold rim glasses so thick they make his eyes buggy, starring down from the spun-up piano stool playing his hart out.

—pull your nitey up, he panted.

i did.

—not a bleamish, Lary said. Probly more about his music then about me. i felt a litel turned on, myself. The way he trilled the keybord without any attention to what key he was in made my legs tingle. i coud feel the viberations thru the bed. i wanted to shift my legs around so i did. i fealt like raising my pussy up some to get the viberations out of my legs so i did. i thot about Woody and my step daddy and Prof. Boiloo and fealt reddy to melt when all of a sudden the musik stoped like it always dose and Lary jumped over the piano and lit on me, limp as usal, hollering *Lofosh ass!*, wich is Hungery he wont tell me what it means. Dirty, probly. We layed there, me wishing he had some nature going for him. After all, what he want I miss it to. But he has this big hangup & thats why he hired me to get over it. We rolled around for a minute. He layed his glasses on the piano. He smeled like mint shaving loshion and cigars. He was moaning somwhat, and i fealt very unconfortable becase i couldent do his job for him.

—dam, he sayd.

Someday, i know, he woud be able to finish his piece and then he woud have wrote somthing extreamly famous. But not last nite. So thats what hapened for Thanksgiving.

I jest herd on the radio they named that place where they send the rockets up Cape Kenedy. if Lary was darling Jack, he woudent have the troble he does, but he isent. i wish Jack coud come down just once from heven & be with me, but he cant. i wish his spirit coud fill Lary jest once, i woud gladly dye underneath of it. Do you unnderstand, Dear Diry? You are filled with the same blessed spirit. i think i will sneak out & see Woody & Mama Pope, so if i dont writ in you tomorrow, you will know why. i love you. This is the first anaversary of Jacks awful deth. 1 week ago. Diry, you are a week old.

Haf to get some black-&-white creem if i go to Watts, & am about out of dixy Peech. Need som snugy-boots, to, floor cold this time of year.

Dacember 1, Sunday

Dere Diry. This is dum. i got Lary so mad at me, he like to send me back to Watts for good. All i done was snuk out last nite after a practise session i was so lonsome after he went home to his woman. i hich hiked down to Wilshire where i got a bus downtown & transfered to Watts & when Lary found out, he turned brite red & about to pop. – Trixie, if you *ever* do that agayn, this whole projecks scrubbed, he sayd. i asked him why so secret, & he tole me a lot of laws about me being 15, hid on campus, & no gardian & theyre practicly steeling the mony to pay me suposed to spent on other students who got hi grades and been here a long time. All them laws. If Woody was here hed say screw them laws, theyre whiteys law so let whitey obay them. But like Mama Pope sayd, Woody gon end up ded or in the cooler, & you know what hapens when you get in Cheif Parkers cooler. To girls, too. They beat you up or make you put out, with acts. But if Lary or Prof. Boiloo got in the cooler, which isent posable in the first place, they get out on bond. So screw them.

I got a ride with this paddy boy, he driving a mustang like all the other rich boys here. i told Mama Pope whats hapen so far. She sayd, keep it up girl the more you lern there the beter. i didnt see Woody. Him & a couple others left town for a while, something cooking back east. Malcom X bisness, i think. i asked Mama Pope how come Woody got the mony to fly to harlem & she sayd evrybody put in a litel for woody, theres a convention or something.

I stayed all nite with Mama Pope & watcht TV. i seen Hootnany & Gunsmoke & Jacky Gleeson. i like Jacky Gleeson, i seen Gery Lewis to, but i dont like him. Mama lemme sleep on her sofa, but its too hot & stuffy in her room on acount shes old, & dont want the demons to get in so keeps the windows down. I slep in the room where the kristal balls on the table but its always covered but when shes reading it. We split a joint before bedtime. i wanted to take some grass back with me but she wont gimme any. – thats all you need, she sayd, to get busted for pot out in that white mans room on a *colege*!

But i got some jest the same. Russel drove me back & he sold me 5$ worth.

The reason Larys mad, I forgot i gon be locked out Sunday nite, when they lock all the doors, & had to get me a campus cop to let me in, pretending i left some books there. i had to show him my student body card. Now larys all worryed people will find out about us in the practise room. He sayd – Trixie, i coud get *fired* for what you did.

i promise to stay in from now on, but i cant jest stay inside my hole life, & he knows it. He gon try & fine me a beter place. Got som groovy hony-colered snuger boots wich i have on now & cant feel the cold flore at all. bot a new tube of skin-tone.

December 2, Monday

Monday nite. Lary tryed writting his peace again today. No luck, as usal. i am tired, Diry, now tucked in bed in my white nitey *and* snugys lissening to some englishmen called the silver beetles wich i have herd once before on KFWB & like there sound, it is Please Please Me. i wish i could please dere jack tonite. They are my sound. Must tell Lary how i lik Them. Lary wears his gold ring on his rite hand insted his left, says they do that in Hungery, or mabey he just changes it wen he leaves the house. Face all smered with blak-&-white creem & am gon try a 'Bonita' hare do, so hed full of hurty curlers hope Lary doesnt com busting in for a late try, im ugly.

Dacember 3, Tusday

Lary dident hear the silver beetles, he dont lissen to KFWB

Diry, i am geting sick of living here. i am starting reeding on the sly, wich is agaynst Prof. Boiloo who wants to keep me pre-litarate. The radio says Rusia still clayms darling Jack killed by a plot in the Jon Burch Sosiety. Not by 1 misrable Lee Ozwold, but a conspirasy. Well, i hope the ones who done it dye in everlasting hell for there deed! and Malcom X! He sayed the wurst thing in Harlem! He sayd darling Jack set around *twid-deling his thums* while he let terrable deeds be done. Malcom X sayd when darling Jack gunned down, he was only chickens coming home to roost. He sayd the chickens leting peeple dye in Vet-Nam, & Birmingham, where they bombed some litel black girls to deth this week. The chickens got to come home to roost someday, Malcom X & his bad mouth. & i bet Woody standing rite alongside him when he sayd it. Woody, he got a bad mouth, to, if he say things like that agaynst my Jack. Maybe i better put a hex on Malcom X. Diry, you remember this. Your hart is

Jacks hart, & when a arrow of hate peerces his, it peerces you. i ougt to cross Malcom X clean out of you!

(Excuze me for so upset. Flowing, mabey thats partly why, onely 1 Kotex left, wot a dragg living on the campus & the nerest stor about ½ of a mile)

Dacember 4, Wensday

Had lunch with Prof Boiloo & Lary off the campus. Prof Boiloo trying to get me do some tests for him, being pre-litarate & all. He wants to take some pitchurs, too. He will pay me 1.50$ a hour. I hope lary lets me, Lary hardly takes up any time any more. They stoped PT-109 the movy from showing on acount of Jack dying its about him in the war, & Prof Boiloo says a new movy called Docter Strangelove they put off opening till next year, on acount of the assanation, & they dont have that record any more on the radio that was always on about Jack called The Furst Fambly, wich i never liked to much anyhow but was funny about little Bobby playing with toy boats in the bathtub, it mayd him sound like a litel kid. Bobby not near as tall as Jack. Prof Boiloo says the tallest man running for presadent always wins, since Lincon.

cold need a fuzy robe. Maybey Lary will by me 1.

Dacember 5, Thursday

Dere Diry. i am preying for Jacks 2 childern, not the live ones, but the 2 litel tykes i dident even know lived till i herd it over the news. They been raised from where they laid & put to rest forever beside there daddy to confort him in his grave. Litel Patrik Kenedy born this sumer & dyed 2 days later they moved from someplase in Masachusets to Washingtown D.C. & litel baby girl who dyed without even so much as a name way back in 1956 when i was onely 9 yrs old they toke from rode iland.

They put the 2 tykes in the grave by there dady yesterdy morning with Boby & Jaky there, & Teddy who is Jacks brother to.

pimpels geting beter.

Dacember 6, Friday

Well, another week in the life of Trixie Mae, dere Diry, it is Friday the second anaversary of Jacks terrable deth & all day the students not talking about him, they talking about the T G I F club thay belong to wich meens Thank God Its Friday, but i feel jest the other way, blue, 2 hole days coming up with nothing to do. But i do have 1 very good thing to report wich will make you hapy, Diry. Malcom X got kicked out of the Black Muslems for his dirty mouth remark agaynst Jack, so i gess my hex worked. i am gon ask Woody when he gets back what he thinks about Malcom Xs bad mouth. i wish i had a TV tonite i am missing Jack Par, Steve Alen, Sunset Stripe & Roring 20s. going put you to sleep now, Diry, & setel down & blow a joint & lissen to music. it is warm & still. i love you very much. Have my hare up. The Bonita style, wich is low acrost your forhed & a bun in back dident work. Hare to short, or mabey not enuff hare-strate. am trying the *Clasic* tonite, but with my stinky nappy hare . . .??

Dacember 7, Sataday

Lary in trying his best, but give up after about haf a hour & we had the sanwiches he brung. He calls me his kid-dress, wich means Dear, so he says. i wore my blue bikini baby doll *without* the pantys & if that dosent turn him on wot posably wil? i tole him to take me for a ride but he was skeered sombody woud see us & tel his wife. There is lots of hi scool kids satadays, now the crisis over, come for musik lessons of all kinds here, so i can walk around all i want till nite making beleeve im 1 of them.

Tonite i missed Jacky Gleeson & Hootnany & Gunsmoke on TV. i asked Lary for a TV but he sayd my minds beter off without it. Thats all *he* knows, stuck here in this funky practise room. i kin smel his cigars. i am about to smoke the end of Russels pot. Dont know what to do tomorrow, mabey call Russel up & have him come to get me, excep, once i get out, how kin i get in? They got the kind of doors that let you out but not in, like scools. Diry, your all i got, & the radio. I can always diddle, but get tired of that, too. If Mama Pope dident tell me to stay for good luck, id leeve. Lary promised me a robe. got 1 all pikked out, majenta terry clothe with fake fur shag colar.

Clasic haredo looks farely good, with a haf moon curl in front of ech ear, looks a litel bit like Jacky Ks bouffant but her hare much fuller of coarse. Curlers make my head ache.

Dacember 8, Sunday

Thay kidnap Frank Snatra junior today. i wish thay woud kidnap me. At leest it would give me a chanst to go for a ride. Another pissy day, dont even have eny pot left & skared to call Russel. Wonder if Woodys back in town. i herd that song by the Silver Beetles today. I dig. i asked Lary the other day if he liked them & he sayd no. I tole him thay had the best sound around. He tryed to buy me a record of them but they dont have any for sale here. Lary is good harted, but i wish hed take me for a ride. i think skin-tone leeves your skin dry, but mabey it helps the pimpels. *Clasic* haredo lasted 1 day & now its all back to nappy. Shit.

Dacember 9, Monday

Some days, dere diry, nothing hapens like today. i like the days i go to class beter then the days i dont. Lary finely give in & let Prof Boiloo start the tests. Easy $1.50 a hour. Not so easy as turning a trick, but easy, & cleener. He asked me to fit a bunch of wood blocks together today. That was dum, but he claymes after i lern to read, it will be harder to do the same test. i kin talk way beter then i kin rite. Thats why Prof Boiloo wants me for tests. he says i got brayns but missed writting so lern thru my mouth & ears not my eys. He says in 4 yrs he gon chanj me from a pre-litrate brayn to somthing else, and wants me to stay in the lab to test what i do with my mouth in the meentime. He says i gon prove that when sombody writs, they do other things worse. So i am in the lab evry day wich pays good (1.50$), besides meels & bed from Lary, cleen & warm but not to warm. Diry, Prof Boiloo dont know that i am geting litrate a lot faster then he thinks on acount of you, darling litel diry wich i am hiding in Larys piano wich is a good place nobody ever cleens out. Shoud i go back to Watts & live with Mama Pope or sombody? i dont think so.

Dacember 11, Wensday

i missed you yesterday, Diry, not for any reeson except mabey what hapened with Prof Boiloo. i asked Lary if he woud sneek me the bokes we suposed to have for my coarses so i can practise reed but he sayd Prof Boiloo woud freak out if i started to reed before my pre-litrate tests finisht. But i think mabey i kin sneek som from Sharon or 1 of the other students in the lab where we tape. Lary woudent even give me a boke for his MUSIK coarses. Him & Prof Boiloo stik together

i finely found out Prof Boiloo isent only intarested in me for study, but wants some easy pussy like all the rest, i gess like Woody says – dont blame us, chick, we got cursed with needing biches from the Lord, you jest be glad i got a dick. You start worrying when nobody wants your pussy no more. Thats wot Woody says.

Well, dirty, as you can probly gess, im not greeved with cats not wanting me yet, at least the cats im taking coarses underneath of. Like Prof Boiloo. (espesally wen i wear my blue shift with only my new movy star slip unnerneeth & no bra)

Prof Boiloo a very nice man. he wears very dark colored shirts and has a adams apple that jiggels when he talks. He likes me. The first day of classes, he put me in the front row where he coud keep his eye on me, he sayd, and we started waching movies about new ginney (guinee?) where pre-litarate persons go arond with there dicks sticking up and worshiping airplains. (guinea) i am gon get a A in the class for doing specal work. i go to Prof Boiloos office with him and he puts me on a tape recorder and asks me what i think about the movys. i told him those new guinee men woudent last very long if they dident take beter care of there nuts and he laghed and sayd what about the hidrogin bomb and the genrals and the missle plants, we woudent last as long as new guinees if *we* dident take beter care of *our* nuts, so i sayd i gess he is rite, but he used the word difrent He sayd the nice thing about pre-litrate peeple is they live evry minute up to the hilt. He sayd as soon as peeple lerned to writt they get so struck with the past & with the future they forget to care about rite now. In New Guinee they just do whats real when they feel like it, wherever they hapen to be, they dont wear there nuckels out writting about it & having go to a head doctor. They just all live together banging each other a couple times a day and none of the kids have a last name. Prof Boiloo thinks that a neat idea.

He can say that of coarse cause he has a lovly fambly. i seen a picher of his woman and 2 kids on his desk. She a red head with big eyes like a pershan cat, and i cant help wondring what she must think as her man Prof Boiloo talks about pre-litrate hardons to his students all day.

All i haf to do for my A is come with him to his ofice and sit and talk. He keeps looking at me in my blue shift like i was from new ginea somtimes. He asked me about my fambly, wich i already put down in you, diry. Hes always talking color like they do in ANTHRO. He sayd – You got some negro blood in you. your eyes got that heavy, beautiful pig mentashun, & your hare.

What coud i say? He my perfesser and i working for a A

unnerneath of him, but Diry, it bothered me on account of its none of his bisness wot trubble i have with my nappy hare. All i coud say, – My mother was pure west indian.

—Your dad wasent. He must of been part white. Talk about color struck, thats all Prof Boiloo had on his mind yesterdy, like hot for my nappy hair, but i think it was no bra that put his mind to me, you coud see the outline of my tittys. Hes lily white, hisself, & if hes so in love with color, why dident he put his hart where his mouth was? i dident see him marryed to any black woman. All he dose is talk about it. He has a bristely yellow mustach with litel red vains in his cheek, with blue eyes.

—You are also part chinee, he said, you are a suberb combanation of 3 races.

i coudent say enything but boil inside (how much do you got to go thru to get a A?)

—i can see your indian blood in your cheekbones. Indians is chinee you know.

—too bad there isent any new ginnea in me, to.

—mabey there is, he laghed. He has very even teeth and pink lips. He sayd, we'll see about the new guinee in you.

When he sayd that i felt my stomache give a litel twist and all of a sudden my mind had a very real pichure of Prof Boiloo smeared with red and yellow paint, naked with a big, brown hardon jumping up and down around me with rattles on his feat and his tonails growd long. i strapped to the ground, looking up. my stomache gurgled.

—time for lunch, he sayd, want to go to the cafateria?

—Lary says to keep out of pubalick, at least this fall.

—Then we can eat here, he sayd.

We did.

That was a coupel hours ago. Now back in the practise room still feeling groovy. Prof Boiloo is a gentile man. He was reddy to go before we got to our dixy-cup ice cream, wich we never got to, & he likes me a lot & has what it takes even if older. What a releif after Lary! I know i am gon get a A for sure. But ougt i tell Lary? i think i will wait and see what hapens next before i do. i cant get that pichure of his wifes pretty cat eyes out of my hed. His kids age 3 and 6, both boys. He give me 5$, probly to keep me quiet. He dident need to of. he acted sort of surprized wen he found out i dident have any pantys on, only my movy star slip.

Dacember 12, Thursday

Sort of sore. Prof Boiloo never so much as looked up from his desk today.

Well i hope i get to go to New York somday like Woody. Diry, i got wonnerful *news* for you. Thay changed the nayme of the airport in New York to *Kenedy* in honor of you-know-who! i dont know what before, but dosent mater, so if Woody isent home yet, he will of left from *Jacks* airport & i think that is boss, dont you?

But, Diry, we haf to take the salt with the sugar, so i got som bad news for you. The eternal flame on jacks grave went out! Some poor, dum litel cathalic scoolboys taking turns spinkeling holey water on dear Jacks grave & (probly fiting over it) the top come off the bottle & drownded his flame out!! Oh, what a disgusting thing, & mabey poor Jacks sole cryed out in wet angwish when it got slopped, in heven, but i know he forgives. I will bet that litel scoolboy more keerful next time!! But, more good news, Diry, the new presadent say they gon have a half-a-dolar coin in honor of falen Jack. hope to get som & save them for my childern.

Jacky bot a big 14 room house in Washingtown D.C. & the kidnappers let Franky Snotra junor go, unharmed, without collecting eny coin he turned out not to be worth much.

Stil havent got the majenta robe Lary promised. tryed som Long Aid K7 on my hare, seems to work beter then permastrate.

Dacember 13, Friday

This maybe Friday the 13th, but even so, something real boss hapened! i got to move out of Larys practise room to a room with a window. it is cosy & warm & lovly vew of the campus & the town. Some of the campus bildings have colored glass windows like a church – a *real* church, not like Rev Smiths old storefront, & so dose mine. Larys pissed off that i moved, but safer here sence the cops probly staking out the Musik bilding after that nite i snuk in late. so Lary had to give me up, but he gets me wenever he needs me. Prof Boiloo claymes on a good day you kin see clean to the osean from my open window, but Lary sayd no. i never been to the osean, someday i will tell Prof Boiloo & mabey he take me. Dearest diry, let me tell you all about my new room. it has 2 hi windows that if i kin set on the cubbord i kin see out. & drawrs! i just wish i had ½ the cloathes it took to fill the drawrs, on acount of, you see, this room is skinny & long. Suposed to be only a storage room for the Anthro lab, where the students have there tapes & make shows (did i tell you? i am going to be in a show! Thay are going to make a movy pichure of me, & i will be the star! Prof Boiloo jest desided today now that i moved). Well, Prof Boiloo took out some shelves in the great big long cubbord & put in my matress & blankets so i got someplace to ditch in case anybody snoops aroun who isent sposed to. & Prof Boiloo give me the cutest litel box that opens up with a round mirrer on top that i keep my yodora & nockzema & bleech-a-glow, ect, in, & i get to keep the radio, & mabey a TV later, but i got to promise to use the ear fones or els snooping cops will here it wich is a big drag, as you know, dear diry, but will jest haf to get along.

They gon to make my movy in the lab, wich my room opens into, & my room has a key wich even the janaters hasent got.

Now let me tell you where i am rite now: laying in my bed in the cubbord, & in my *new* robe. Yes, Prof Boiloo, not Lary, give me mony for it & i have it on & can feel the majenta shag colar tickeling my throte. soft & warm. i have a nise litel lite over my head & the radio playing Blowing in the Wind by Peter Paul & Marry, while outside cold & blustry. No rats or roaches here. i kin hear my hart beat. beating for the memery of Jack. The flags still flying in Morning at ½ mast. i do like lovly Jackie K sayd she was, go into morning for 1 hole year! She isent going out noplace for a year. Neether am i. i am going wear black someplace always on me for 1 yeer excep in bed. i have 1 pr of black pantys but need more, i will ask Lary or Prof Boiloo to get me some more in honor of darling JFK, that way i kin stay in morning without calling attenshun. 3 weeks today sence you-know-what. Shoud i writ to Jacky for a pitchur of Jack F. K.? i here she gives them out to peeple.

Dacember 14, Sataday

Watts.

Safe at Mama Popes in the ally bak of the stores.

Mama Pope jest sayd, what you writting down, & i tole her & all she sayd is hmmp. Little kids think she a witch like i use to – wen i come in today they tole me not to touch her chain-link fense or Id get killed. They think she got it wired. They run past with sticks against it for noise, but wont touch with there hands. And wen the beer bottles stuck in the ground moan out front like theyre spose to in the wind to scare the moles, they think its gosts. Mama lets them think so like she used to me. She dont like them kids sneeking in & setting on the white plaster lion by the porch steps. They plage her avacato tree something terrable, to. I remember that time i snuck in & dug up all them beer bottles to see if they had roots, like the flowers. *All* of them. I must of been about 3. But she dident whup me. She never whups kids.

dreemy. desided to let my hare go natral. We had a joint. im setting here smiling in my new robe & snugys. Mama Pope smels like colard greens & warm, like my moma use to smell at dinner, mixed in with the bacon frying, & like milk left over from tits. Diry, my moma had arms like pillows. then at nite, perfume. i use to think she went to tower-cassels like in picher books where you coudent get in without smelling sweet, why she wore the perfume. Turning tricks, thats all. I wonder if she turned tricks while she still had milk from me?

hot here, we ech had some of Mama Popes wild irish rose wine for diner. Shes still watching jonny carson or some smart mouth. Poor Mamas trying to get over the fidgets, wich she offen has feering doom. Woody says somday he gon put his heel thru jonny carsons fayce, the onely smart mouth he likes is Louis Lomacks.

Dere Diry, i will put this page *in* you wen i get back to the campus. Lary & Prof Boiloo let me stay with Mama Pope sense scools out for chrismess, but i haf to be back on Tusday for some tests. Woody isent back from New York yet but do soôn, Russel says. i wonder about Russel. Hes a fulltime pusher now, but Woody in the Black Moslems & the Black Moslems gaynst drugs. Mama Popes rocking in her chare trying to calm after her vision. She had a vision tonite that something gon hapen to hurt lots of people in L.A. soon. i hope it dont hurt Mama nor me, nor Russel, nor Lary (nor his wife) nor Prof Boiloo nor sharon my new frend at scool. i hope the gost of darling Jack preteck these peeple thru the nite. Mama Popes sofas got lumps. i give her $10 for staying till tusday, wich i got from Prof Boiloo.

Dacember 16, Monday

i got some *things* to tell you, Diry. Woodys back, but not for long. Last nite he toke me over to a meeting where they planning to give whitey a ruff time. Not here in L.A. but back east. Thay made a lot of fun about the dam what bursted a couple days ago, gess i forgot to tell you, thats what Mama Pope so fidgity & upset the other nite, she felt in her bones something bad hapen, & sure enuff, yesturday that dam burst & killed a whole lotta people & recked 200 houses, you coud wach it on TV chanel 5. Anyhow, thay laffed about it at the meeting.

Woody sayd if whitey thinks its bad that *dam* bursted, jest wait till the *black* dam burst, & the black hate stored up sence slavery pours its black waters over the busted dam. *Then* youll see peeple dye & houses burn make the dam look like nothing. Woody sayd he going back east rite after Christmas & mabey take 1 or 2 of them cats from the meeting with him, if thay got guts.

Diry, whats gon hapen to Woody? Mama Pope says she dont know, but she sees blood acrost his life. Rev Smith was there, but dont say much. Woodys got his new chin beerd, sort of. Some of them cats wear pretty beards now & beeds & embroydry blouses & afro capes. Woodys wiskers pretty thin. He says he gon haf to settle for what hair he got on his balls, wich isent as much as me, if you want the truth. Later we went to Woodys room over Hole-a-go-go. Mama Pope chewed Woody out for screwing me like she always do, but it isent her bisness & we never do it without a rubber. Besides, what do she know? Woody says she dont have any call over me, she just somebody the county payed to take care of me once, & nows on the skids. Woody says shes bad for me, & when she starts talking Down Home, to shut my ears, thats finished, all that shit about how her daddy stole the horse & rode a hunderd miles with her mommy & then kicked the horse back toward home not to steal it & walked the other 2 hunderd, as if that was something *smart* & *good* insted of keep the horse like he shoud. But Mama never whupped me & I like her for that. I tole Woody. Even that time I berryed my new doll they give me after the funeral. Nobody found it till step daddy come over to hoe for peas. He crushed rite into the head. The ground made her hare all moldy. I seen it. When he come after me with the hoe, Mama Pope woudent let him touch me. Woody sayed – it was a white doll? Yes. I berryed it cause I seen my moma berryed, thats why.

After Lary & Prof Boiloo its nice to get back in bed with Woody he dont mess around besides i feel so embarassed with perfesser men, theyre so smart assed & all, you never know what theyre thinking, but always thinking. Woody jest lets hisself go, & wispers to me that im still the best body around. i wonder. i dont do nothing. i jest let him rip whatever i got on, off – my blue bikini baby doll & let him do it, & come when he dose. He says thats all i haf to, with my looks & my skin, but he pokes fun about my skinny ass – i gess he likes real oil bags – & always says im too lite to be a self-respecting nigger chick, but hes color struck hisself, he likes lite no matter what he says in front of Rev Smith & them other cats about black is bootiful. Diry, Woodys got a big pecker that makes you skared to look at it, but he treets me good. We split a joint he made me promise not to tell any of the moslims, & then we talked & done it again later. twice. I asked him about back east & he tole me all the big things going to hapen, but to keep my flap shut, so i am not telling *no*-one except you, dere diry, not even Mama Pope. She kin find out wot she wants from her own kristal ball & not from my lips. But diry, i love you best, so will tell *only you.*

i fergot to chew his nigger ass out like i planed about Malcom X. That is, i remembered to when they talked about Malcom X over at Big Rons house where they had the meeting, but skared to say anything in front of them about 'the chickens coming home to roost' – you remember. Then later i fergot. Woody sed Malcom X gon get it 1 of these days, hes making a big move in the Black Moslem. Rev Smith sayd Malcom X got a bad mouth, but Woody sayd, you jest wait till nex summer, what Malcom X sayd about mister charley so far, & them chickens home to roost, will sound like down home, compared to nex summer. Later i asked Woody about nex summer. Woody sayd the people down hom gon rebel nex summer & he gon be there. He sayd for me to come along & i sayd, okay, you pay the way. He laghed. He sayd – Pay your own way, you cute bich, we all got to pay our own way from now on. But he dident pay his own way to New York. I ment it, too, if he wants me, he pays my way. He must of popped his nuts 4 times. I gess he really miss me. He tole me he liked my hare natral, but mabey jest sayd that.

Dacember 18, Wensday

Very blue. Woody so mean to me yesterday after being so nice the day before & now hes gone, & my face all broke out with pimpels. Why, Diry, why? Why cant men be desent 2 days in a row? Yesterdy we went uptown to the head bilding of scools & a litel bunch of no-count protesters march up & down with signs about intagrating scools. Then they set down in the doorway (all white) & the Man hawled about 25 off in wagons. Woody & Big Ron & me, & a couple girls naymed Leona & Beverly who was at the meeting the other nite stode acrost the street. it was all over in a minute. Big deal. They arrest you & get a sheet on you down at Cheif Parkers Palace for what? Just setting down on some dum steps.

Big Ron sayd – why the fuck you drag my ass up here to see this, Woody? Woody sayd – i dident drag *your* ass up here, i dragged these girls. Trixie Mae, he sayd, what chance you think a nigger chick like you got out at your colege, when thay treet there own kind like this? Throw them in jail for setting down? & you, he sayd to Leona & Beverly. They both went to L.A. State to be teachers, it turned out. You to, look at these white cats fucking around with signs and set-ins. You seen what there own duty consious cops done, you think theres eny hope for this fucked up rotten sosiety from *them*? If they throw each other in jail for this? Wheres our freedom for speech gone?

Ron sayd – You dont haf to talk to *me*, Woody

Woody sayd – Its dam well time our wemen got behind us for something besides somebody to jugg. Then he sayd to me – go on, fuck your lousy prefessers, thats okay with me, but when they get thru with you, i want you to shuck *them* out, not the other way around, you hear.

i tole Woody i wasent fucking the prefessers. i lye somtimes.

He sayd – Leona & Beverly, where you get off teaching in *white* scools?

Leona sayd – Thats where the mony is, Woody.

And always will be, i sayd.

Then Woody slapt me acrost the mouth. He called me a dirty litel slut for saying that, but Big Ron & the girls tole him to cool it. The Man was watching.

Beverly sayed – youd have one hell of a time flying back & forth to New York by flapping your arms, Woody. Where you think your ticket mony come from? Dont give us the badmouth for earning our mony our own way.

Woody made me cry, all rite, with that slap in the face, but I beleeve it. What makes him think he'll ever get mony? Hes jest jelous about me & Lary & Prof Boiloo & hates it i got new cloths. They dumped me off here at the campus. He dident even look at me, & hes gone back east agayne for a long time. What a terrable ending & how mean. Diry, is Woody rong or am i? i think Woodys rong. You got to have mony & *however* you get it helps. Mama Pope says Woody gon have some big yeers ahead. Well, Diry, i herd *that* talk before, & unless your some Hary Belafontey ready to eat shit with a smile you aint going nowhere. Woody knows that in his hart, too, but skared to say so. *He cannot eat shit.* The radio tonite says 2,500 blacks marched in Adlanda Gorgia tody. Martin Luther King says there gon be trubble till the Problem gets solved. Woodys rite in a way. im not gon spend my time toting signs. i kin do better here with Prof Boiloo & Lary. i got a door key now so dont haf to crawl in windows. i am now cozy in my litel cubbord. i have you & my radio (no TV). i look nice in my pink nitey but wisht my hair strayter. Woody is 7 yrs older then me & at the rate hes going will be a old man & mabey ded before i be 20. Lary lots older then Woody but skin lokes younger. He stays out of the sun. Prof Boiloo even older than Lary & has a teeny shake to his hands from booze, i think. It is nerely Crismas. Some girls my age would miss Crismas, to be alone, but i dont. Crismas was never eny good, that i remember. Moma dyed on Chrismas. I slept in Mama Popes bed after that. She put teeth in a glass. She smelled like old selery. I dont mind that smell. The times i wet the bed she put a clean cotton blanket on that still had sunshine in it, or put me to sleep on the sofa under the purple blanket with the purple eyes in it, that she croshayed. On the radio today it says the day that darling Jack dyed in Dalas Nov. 22 a big ad in the paper caled him a Commy. THAT IS A LYE! Diry, Jack was *not* a Commy & if he was, done it for peeple like me. Let them say wot they want, Jacks sole is safe from hurt, & plenty peeple sore about the ad they let run in the paper the day he dyed. Some peeple start things they cant finish, like Beverly told Woody after he popped off at me about getting mony from Prof Boiloo.

Dacember 19, Thursday

Well, this isent the onely place they got black riots. They had 1 in Rushia yesterday.

More tests from the Anthro students today. They had me making up words to musik as i went along. Sharon says later, when i get litrate, Prof Boiloo will make me do all these tests over agayn & show how the words i do then, in 3 yrs, arnt so good as the ones i do now. Well, we'll just see about that. i havent wrote a pome for a long time. Usaly pomes jest *come* espeshally wen im hungery. i gess i havent been hungery for a long time. Dose it have to do with easier to make up poems if you cant writ? i think im not gon be eny taller than i am now. i am 5 feet 2, wich is enuff for a girl. Woody isent very tall neither, compared to Big Ron.

I think nockzema helping my pimpels.

Dacember 20, Friday

Diry, i done it. i wrot to Jacky K for a pitchur of her dere late husband. i hope i here. i mayled it down at Alphys where i eat somtimes. Sharon left for Chrismas. She lives up by Frisco. i think she rich but dont like to say so. This her 3rd colege i think. She quit & bumed around for a while, she calls it. She can always go home & get cleened up wen she tired of buming around. i think she had a low high on grass yesterday. Her eyes loked red & swole. i am sory Sharon gone. i like her best. The others okay, i gess, but when the others test you, like today on what words i call certain things by, compared to words regular colege kids use, they tune out & i feel jest like a piece of meat with a mouth. When Sharon tests you, its like your *both* working at it. Sharon has a car.

Dacember 21, Sataday

Lary drug me back to the practise room today. Same old stuff, but Im not his 'Kid-dress' any more. Hes mad lately, not onely at Prof Boiloo for moving me, but he says the Commys taking over the U.S. of A. like they done in Hungery when he left. He says the Black Muslems trying to help take over the U.S. of A. like the reds alreddy took over Cuba. His wifes sik from it.

His wife sure sik a lot. If Lary thinks things bad now, i coud tell him a thing or 2 about wot Woody says for next summer. But i wont. Only to you, diry. Lary hasent got a hard on all fall, & i laid there with my yelow dress unbutoned all the way doun, wich ougt to turn anybody on. I ougt to tell Woody, that would make him feel good by comparason, the rat.

Dacember 22, Sunday

i get my choise to spend Crismas here or with Mama Pope, Lary says. For some reeson i deside to spend it here. i think the reeson is, diry, mabey Lary or Prof Boiloo will give me somthing for Crismas if i stay here (seen a *beautiful* blue reversable wool cote with roled colar at Orbacks) & besides, Woody gone.

cold out. i walked around part of the campus today in my terquoize strech pants & terquoize sweter, but jest my old broun cote & a litel dog folowed me part way back. If i had a dog, i woud take good care of him. He was brown & fuzzy & probly belong to somebody who miss him, mabey my old broun cote reminds him of his mama. He sniffed my feet. jest had my scuffs on.

1 month today!

Dacember 23, Monday

well, the flags here gone to the top of the poll today. All will forget. The morning over for our falen leader JFK but on the radio they sayd some awful man who use to be a genaral dident go into morning for JFK at all, but insted put his awful flags cleen to the top of the poll this hole month while the rest of us live in sorrow to the memry of our falen hero. If they let people like that run free they outent lock up Rev King like they do.

desided to put my hare up agin. Natral jest too frizzy on me. Head hurts.

Dacember 24, Tusday

On the news darling JFKs last will, he give haf his mony to Jackie, she gets all the cash from it, & the other haf for his 2 litel childern Carolyne 6 – John John that sweet baby whos 3 years old. i am glad Jack left plenty mony for his fambly so they kin live in dignaty of his sacred memory forever. Still havent herd from Jacky & the pitchur, but shes probly busy aroun Crismas buying presents for all her fambly & frends.

Dacember 25, Wensday

Chrismas. Lary with his fambly. Prof Boiloo went back east someplace, they allways having meetings in Anthro. a very cold morning. i kin see clean acrost town to the osean. most mornings its too fogy. Wish i coud see Woody today or mama pope, but i mayde my choise. Mabey Lary will come with presents later. a new cote?? Prof Boiloo wont be back till New Years. He left enuff mony for grocrys till then. i ate dinner at Alphys. The girl sayd, how come you eating Crismas dinner all alone? I sayd, we waiting till tomorrow for our dinner, wen my daddy who is out of town, gets home. i had turky, it was awful dry, but i had 3 cokes. Diry, i will tell you some secret things. Step daddy use to buy me off with cokes for not telling Mama Pope what he done to me. That was when he toke me away from her place i had a game called Waiting For Him where i coud pray cars to turn into the house. Wen they turned in the driveway & hedlites flashed on the cieling i thought i had Prayed him Home car, car, come, come, car, car, come, come. After the TV busted another way i had was Driving Him Home to set in that old car out back of that place that hadent run for all year & the tires flat, Driving Him Home nite after nite. But Driving Him Home dident work so good as laying on the porch Praying Him Home car car, come come, car car, come come. The rule was, if the hedlites flashed on *you*, the spell busted, so thats why you scrooched under the window wen the car turned in, to keep the hedlites off. i use to dream about the place they take old cars to, lined up behind a fense. It had to do with putting a coke bottle in me, where they berryed Moma.

got a hony colered haf-slip to mach my hony-colered bra, jest in case i need a match somtime.

Dacember 26, Thursday

Gess Wot! Lary brung a TV. it isent mine but i got the lone of it. Lary brung lunch & sayd if we go practise for a wile, he got a surprize. So we had a tail-all, tho nothing as usal, i tryed playing with him even, but no luck. i think Lary is finisht, his nature gone forever, pore man. Mabey his sik wife the reeson. Anyhow, he played his piano & i layd there as usal wigling around trying to get him exsited, & hoping he had brung me a present (cote mabey?) & after a wile we quit. Well, Lary says – You kin have the present anyway, wich was a neet portable TV all my own (to use). i dident need Lary after that. He went home to his wife & her pills & sik hedaches & i snuggeled down to Chanels 2, 4, 5, 7, 9, 11, 13, 22 & 28! The pitchur reel good except 9. i got it in a shelf acrost from my bed cubbord &, Diry, i coudent wayte to tell you. I seen Hukelberry hound, Rawhide, Dr. Kill Dare, Lawman, Pery Mason, The Nurses, The Jimmy Deen show & Sid Seezer tonite & am redy for bed so goodnite dear Hart. Hope to here by tomorrow from Jacky.

Dacember 27, Friday

Seen Rout 66, Berks Law, Twilite Zone (verry cool) (& skary) The Prise is Rite, Alfred Hich Cock (verry skary too) Jak Parr (my favrote, somtimes) Steve Allen (i like him but his gests kooky) Jony Carson (ug!) Sunset Stripe. i swicht chanels a lot to pik the best 1. i dident wach some of them all the way. Well, no more new letters in Prof Boiloos office till Mon. i gess Jacky too busy to send pitchurs anymore.

Dacember 28, Satarday

Went out looking for that fuzzy brown puppy, in old cote. Dident find, but steped in a dog turd. Dident see it till i got home & it smeled. Ate at alphys. Had a hamberger on Rye & 3 cokes. i wish Prof Boiloo or Sharon or sombody woud come back. put up my hare but in wet wether kinks rite up. Wached Jacky Gleeson, Hootnany (groovy), the Dafenders, Gunsmoke, Jery Lewis. Jery Lewis stinks. i here theyre taking him off. Seen a good movy about Mars. The Mars peeple was beter than the erth people.

pimpels nerely gone. Havent used skin-tone in a long time & seem jest as lite – probly being winter is the difrence.

Dacember 29, Sunday

Seen My Favrote Marsian, Walt Disny Presents, Ed Sulivan (he gon have the Beetles on in *6 wks. must not miss*). Judy Garland Show (ug), Candid Camera, wich i like but gives me the creeps. i even wached the Lone Ranger. i gess Jacky run out of pichures, or too busy to answer. i wonder if you haf to be cathlik to have her answer?

Mahalia Jackson singing We Shal Overcome all over the place on TV. Forgot to tell you, Dina Washintoun dyed last week. She was maryed to Nite Trayn Layne. My step daddy knowed her. took drugs.

Dacember 30, Monday

Nope, nothing from Jacky. Well, why shoud she send a pitchur to anybody who writs? Seen Truth or Consekwenses, Your First Impreshun, Star for To Day, Day in Court, To Tell the Truth, Queen for a day. Felt lousy. Got the curse, & *no Kotexes*! Just layd around waching TV. Ate 4 hershy bars. Got haf sik. Slept thru diner & now its 12 oclock i am wide awake, jest finisht watching Have Gun Will Travel, I Got a Secrete, Divorse Court, & Ded or Alive. i feel more ded then alive. i am sik of waching TV. i wish i had mony to go with Woody. i woud even pay my own way. LBJ down on his ranch in Texas where they killd poor Jack. i hope he is happy. i am sad. How meny Fridays gone by i dident even comemrate Jacks memry? Well, i am going wear black pantys all yeer. That is eesier then remembering Fridays. Besides, wot do Fridays meen? it is months & yeers, not weeks, that we remember our Jack. ('i'll bet even Jacky forgets some now, once in a while)

Dacember 31, Tusday

Diry, it jest about 12 oclock New Yers.

i wached new yeres on TV. Red Skelton best. Seen MacHales Navy, Petticote junksion, The Corupters. The Datectives, Surfside 6. Diry, Hapy New Yr! in the New Yere of 1 9 6 4 i am going to keep you by my side, & your going be my best frend. i am going to stay faythful to the memery of Jack by:

1 – not geting so mad at peeple, like i got at Woody
2 – staying here in the colege & mayking frens
3 – trying be frens with white girls like Sharon even if Woody dont like it
4 – *not* leting peeple fuck me so much. i'll let Woody, but not russel. i wil let Prof Boiloo if he wants, *but only if he helps me in meny ways.* i will keep trying to help Lary, but thats difrent, that is a job.
5 – not wach TV so much
6 – quit diddaling, mabey will help the pimpels

Diry, wen i cloze my eyes i see the yere 1 9 6 4 like a horse shoe loop. The Spring of the yere goes down 1 side, the sumer acrost the curved botom, the fall up the other. i kin see 1 9 6 4 lined up with the other yeres like horse shoes in a strayt line til a hole century is lined up. Then at the end, they take a quick tern & start another century but i cant see the end of that one. All the yeres hang in black spayce. i kin see back only till just befor i was born, & i kin see ahed till about 2020 maybe, i got to look out the corner of my eye to see them, but i can. Mama Pope says she sees the yeres stowed in a black feather pillow in heven, she says. The yeres fall out 1 by 1 floating to earth shoved around by the wind. The fallen feathers lay in a heep in a black forest. She says as the year-feather falls you can blow & blow it till you pass out from dizzy, but still cant keep it from falling by Dec 31.

i will make a list of wot i own, to start 1 9 6 4. i own $21.05 cash left over from wot Prof Boiloo give me. i got the TV (lone), my radio, my clothes (i will not put down all my clothes) (yes i will, i got 4 nylons, 1 garter belt, 3 prs shoes (the black flats, the scuffs & my good blue ones) & my shagy boots, 3 braseres, 6 pantys (4 black for Jack), both sweters, the blue one & the other one, my yelow dress, my white blouse, my pink ruffeled blouse, my pink hip huggers with the wide blak belt, my blue shift, niteys (white long one & blue baby doll), 2 prs strech pants, my movy star slip, & new ½ hony colered slip, my brown wool cote, my old pink bath robe & new majenta tery clothe. i got my scool stuff, my toiletreys like Crest, feeenamint, nervine, pomade, asprin, ect, Arrid, black-&-white creem, Artra, Vicks syrup, nockzema ect wich i wont put down all, like my comb & brush & Ultra-Sheen, & i got *you*, diry. Oh yes, i got my purse & all the stuff in it, Woodys pichure, ect, wich i wont nayme. i have them record albums down at Woodys (Mavelettes, Sam Cooke, Beech Boys ect) wich i will probly never get back. My garnet ring. i think Prof Boiloo give me the clock for myself to keep. But not the matress, ect, of coarse. Thats about all enybody needs, & i could be a lot wurse off.

if i had wot i reely wanted, i would have stuff like a car like Sharons, a house all my own, color TV, clothes clothes clothes like that new reversable cote & dress with fur sleeves at Orbacks & more shoes, a dog & a cat, mony to spend all the time, a pass so i coud fly enywheres in the world i wanted (surprize Woody back east) a hi-fi & all the records i wanted. A white fur cote, lots of shoes, a big car like a Caddy wich a shofer woud drive, a big bedroom with a *huge* round bed & a bathtub sunk in the floor. A coke machine rite in the house. No pimpels & long hare. A pass to eny movy. Get to meet Jacky & talk to her about Jack. Babysit with Caroline & Jon Jon sometime, jest to talk. Drive up in my Caddy behind Woody & honk the horn. Get Lary to come. Buy out the Hole-a-Go-Go & star there. Be a famous movy star. Get to be reel good frends with Sharon & have her to my house. Buy a color TV for Mama Pope. Have a boy – 2 boys – & a girl & have Woody get a good job & stay home.

1964

Janyuary 1, Wensday

Wached the rose bowl parade on TV. Like to seen it in color, mabey next yere. Dwite Isenhower Grand Marshel, & some cat had them skared he was gon demenstrate agaynst segregashun. Wish i could be a rose quean or a princess, but its all segragated. Went for a walk. Need a new cote. Never have saw that litel fuzzy brown pupy dog agayn. Scool tomorrow. Thank goodness. Sharon will be back.

Janyuary 5, Sunday

Dear Diry

I havent wrote lately on account of I am plane embarased wot a dum writter i am. Wot i been doing latly with Prof Boileau (*thats* how his name spelled) is teling him about Watts. We been talking about the Problem & the Man & wot its like being down in Watts & Woody & Mama Pope & all this time he been taping me. Now last week he showed me how to start & stop the recorder & is having me writ down evrything i sayd, like i think it ougt to be wrote. Thats wen it hapened.

You shoud of herd them students laff & laff at how i writ. Sharon Atwatter dident laff but them others did & they are jest all students thereselfs. But thanks to Prof Boileau they shut up kwik. He says now I gon change from Orel to Writing. He says he gon test my braynes & my style & how i think about things wile i change over & that way theyll know wot writting dose to your brayne. but if i writ this bad why keep a secrit diry? i'll tell you why keep a secrit diry, on account of sense darling Jack is gone & sense i moved over here in spite of Lary, i havent anybody in the world except my diry for frendship. i jest want you to know, diry, how much i still love you, in spite the mess i make out of you.

Prof Boileau keeps talking about some Marshal named Macloon. Prof Boileau says he gon write Marshal Macloon about me that he has a test case for the new kind of person in the U.S. of A. on account of im a pre-litarate find, but smart, rased on TV, & therfore electriconic. Well, litel dose he know i am practising on my own to get litrate, dere diry, & you are doing it for me (& me for you) we will show Prof Boileau & his Marshal Macloon who kin rite & who is only electriconic! I have desided to go all the way. i asked Mama Pope yesterdy if i ought keep writting the diry & she sayd go ahed. The new Cival War coming soon, she sayd, so girl, you put it all down. It might make up for Mama Pope never wrote in her life. Wen her fokes lived in texas planting corn with sticks, they dident have scools. All she can put down is her hex marks & magic marks.

i will. i am verry sory diry for not writing latly but hope you unnderstand how embarassed they made me laffing at my writing. Love you.

Janyuary 11, Sataday

Dere Diry. im awful sory, but i been so bizy latly i jest havent had time to tell you everything.

1 – last sataday seen Mama Pope. Sharon took me down in her sports car but i made her drop me off on the bus line so they woudent razz me for showing up with Sharon who they will call jest another white girl if they see her. bad enuff being at the colege without them seeing Sharon (diry, she is blond & very fare skinned)

2 – Seen Big Ron at the Hole-a-go-go Sun. He sayd Woodys in Gorgia stirring up some kind of mess or other. Still out of jail but??? for how long?
3 – Mon-Tus-Wns ect. Scool. They bin leting me reed anything. i tryed starting the book we are sposed to reed for Anthro 150 but ... Jesus Crist! like i sayd before, Prof Boileau promised me a A for jest being here, & the same with Lary, so i will wayte a wile before trying reed. Lary & Prof Boileau took me over to a Prof. where they teech teechers & give me some esier bokes. They are ment for cats like Ritcherd (the cook at the Hole-a-go-go) who *reely* cant reed. Theyre about pro fotball, ect, wich Ritchard pays attenshun, but use litel esy words. i can reed them okay, but who cares about pro fotball? i am going to reed the book in Anthro 150 anyway if it kills me. Sharon sayd she woud help.
4 – Dident wach much TV, but nex week there is a show *i am not going to miss. Jacky* will be on (i gess she never got my card asking for a pitchur. Shoud i writ agayn? no. Once is enuff)
5 – i am not going menshun this any more, but Lary & me practised tail agayn yesterday. In my blue shift hiked cleen up to my nek. No luk as usal. i think he ougt to quit trying, but he does whenever he gets pissed at the reds. This time, over a plot to take over africa.
6 – i forgot to tell you. That senatar naymed Gold Water says he gon try to get the bid to run for Presadent. Mama Pope says *he* the one gon get the bid agaynst LBJ next time & wen i tole Prof Boileau he sayd – Not a chanse, the republacans wont nomanate *him*. But Big Ron beleeves Mama Pope & hes 'tick-eled pink' like Prof Boileau says sometimes. Ron says the quiker Rasists like Gold Water run, the quiker the cival war come on, wich finely gon free the colored peeple or kill them. Wich is why i put it in, Diry, to tell you i dont want Woody dying in no cival war, & if Gold Water running makes that so, i hope he dosent run. Prof Boileau says he hasent got a chanse anyhow. Rockyfellers gon run for the republacins, Prof Boileau says, & hes smart.

January 13, Monday

Still reeding. Stayed in all week end. rayned. Hare up in curlers, jest trying to keep it a *litel* bit strate in all this wet. Lary come by last nite but we jest talked, dident even diddel. He called me 'kid-dress' agayn. i here on TV where the hotels in Adlanta, Gorgia, gon let negroes stay there from now on. i wisht i had Woodys adress, i would tell him to go stay in a hotel, if he had the mony. The reson he slapped my face when i tole him the whites woud always have the mony was, he knowed i was rite.

January 14, tusday

i got it!

From jacky! & tomorow i will see her on TV. it come in todays male, a *lovly* picture of darling Jack, not serous, but with a nice smile on his face in color. it is a reely boss picture & i am going cherish it forever, i got it pasted in the cubbord so i kin see Jack wen i lay down. it come in a brown paper envalop (saving it, to) & on it sayd: 'DEAR GOD, PLEASE TAKE CARE OF YOUR SERVANT, JOHN FITZGERALD KENNEDY.' Dere God, plese *do* take care of him forever more so wen we all go to heven he will be there to take our hans!

wonder if pimpels & diddeling has a connexion?

January 15, Wensday

I seen Jacky *jest* now. But what a shit hole time i had trying get the god dam TV working rite! i got the pichure okay (she was on 3 chanels) but no *sound*! This is the *first* time my TV hasent worked good, & had to hapen wen Jacky come on. She set in a lether chair with Boby & Tedy on a sofa, by the fire, but wen they talked, nothing! Well, as it turned out, it wasent my set, but somebody messed up the show. i fliped to Chanel 7, but the same. Finely i went to Chanel 2, *they had sound but by then i missed* most of it! Luckely they replayed it in Chanel 4 & 7 so got to here it all, finely, but still shaky from being so mad. She was verry good. She had on a black suit & all the jewlry she wore was her weding ring. That was nice. She sayd she got lots of letters (like the 1 i sent, for the picture) & she sayd wen she felt blue, she red some of them & she woud never forget how nice we bin to her. Then she sayd, all His brigt lite gone from the world. I cryed agayn like wen it hapened. So did she, almost. Boby & Tedy was very good. They mostly jest set there. Well, i feel now like something is ended. i got his picture at the foot of my matress, & seen Jacky on TV & it is now cleen next yere. Somthing is heeling, but there will always be that tender spot for him.

Love you, Diry.

January 20, Monday

Final test week. In colege, at the end of the term, all the clases get out while peeple do there final tests. i dont have to do any. We had one in Dance & Rythm, but that was nothing. i migt even get a A in that. i dont have to take any tests in ANTHRO 150 & ANTHRO 204 (both Prof Boileau) nor in MUSIK 105 *or* MUSIK 309 (both Larys). i get A's in them to help keep me in scool wen i take coarses not from unnderneeth of Prof Boileau & Lary, wich will meen very low grades, & you haf to keep your avarage up. Lary all upset on acount of it looks like Panama is going Commy. Lary such a nut on this. if Lary only knowed wot Woody had in mind for rite here in L.A., he would quit wetting his pants about Panama!

Desided to save mony for that blue reversable cote at Orbacks.

January 25, Friday

Final tests over. i sayd to Sharon by acksident that i hadent never bin to the Osean. When i sayd i lived in L A all my time, she jest bout fliped. So she took me in her car to the osean, along with Lily, who is another student here. The Osean is somthing else! Diry, it is perfeckly flat & where it ends you cant see the difrence between water & sky. If you want to go to heven like Jack is, now i know how. you jest start off over the water from Santa Monika & if you keep walking, youll walk rite up into the sky. The sand is boss, & the waves roll in chasing each other & me & Sharon & Lily went barefoot, but the water cold & your feet get sticky from the water afterwards, Sharon says thats the salt. She tole me to taste it. it tastes jest like salt, but the air around the osean smells more like mens scum, or wet plaster. That may not sound prety, but the osean isent entirly prety, but wether its entirly prety or not, you got to pay *attenshun* to it, & thats wot makes it prety. I can smell salt in my hare, & it makes it kinky.

January 26, Sunday

i feel kind of sik. On the nite news it showed a fite in Adlanta & im skared Woody was in on it. Some cats tryed eating at a restrant & i seen the cops & a son of a bitching Yakoo bouncer drag some wemen out by there skirts & hair. They hurt 6 of them. I seen the bouncer hit the girls over there heds with a chare & nobody stoped him. You coud here the peeple laghing behind them. i felt sik to my stomache waching. i feel so sory for them girls but they was grown up big enuff to know wot hapens wen you cross Whitey down home. They had no call being there in the first place. They sayd snik put it on, wich is the new thing Woodys working for this yere. i hope Woody wasent there. Wached Ed Sulivan. *2 weeks* till the Beetles.

January 27, Monday

Lary had a paper this morning wich showed pictures of them 6 girls in Adlanta. i dident see Woody in any. Lary sayd it was started by Commys so i shut up about Woody, i dont think he is a Commy, & Larys such a *nut* on the thing. He said the way the guvernment trys to force rules on peeple, like who kin eat in your restrant, & who cant, is sosialism wich leads rite to Communism. Thats the Hungery in him. 3 of them girls had to go to the hospital, it sayd. Shoud i of been there alongside Woody? Dont know. Asked Prof Boileau about diddeling & pimpels & he says no conexion. Am trying Perma-Strate 1 more time.

January 28, tusday

Well, i'll be surprised if Woody aint been busted by now. They arested 116 in Adlanta yesterday. Mama Pope & the others will probly be hearing for bail mony. Poor Woody, i wisht he'd stayed home, going around stiring up other peeples trubbles. But thats Woody. Dere Diry, remember, you are the sole of Jack & owe your life to His memry, help me prey for Woodys safty thru the intersesion of darling Jack from Heven!

January 31, Friday

i signed up for my new classes for spring term. Lary & Prof Boileau had a big argument about wether i ougt to get alowed to go thru the lines you haf to, to get into classes, & Lary finely lost so him & Prof Boileau done it agayn. This time i get

Coarse		Name	Credats	Teacher
ANTHRO	307	Indians of Calif	(3)	Prof B.
MUSIK	399	Indapendant Study	(3)	Lary
MUSIK	309B	Amer Foke Musik	(2)	Lary
ANTHRO	306	Indians of Amer	(3)	Prof B
P.E.	169	Danse & Rythm	(1)	Miss Lench
			12	

It is about the same as last time with 2 coarses unnerneath Lary & 2 unnerneath Prof Boileau. He dosent expeck me to reed the book but i jest mite fool him.

Him & Lary got in another fite about how much longer i got to go on sleeping in the closet. Lary thinks i ougt to get a pad of my own – so he can come over, i think – but Prof Boileau says thats more dangerus then staying here. Shes onely 15, he sayd (16 in 2 weeks) & if we get caght keeping her in a pad we'll end up in San Kwinton, wheras if she stays here, she's always part of the labertory. He told Lary they kept a old indian naymed Ishy up in a museum for a long time at Berkaly, & that was okay.

—Yea, Lary sayd, but Trixie Mae isent a old indian.

—Oh, you notised, Prof Boileau sayd.

—& dont tell me *you* havent noticed, Lary tole him.

Well, they argued for a wile & desided to let me stay, wich is what i wanted. i also tole them i wanted a new cote from Orbacks. it is lonly, yes, but what they dont know & you nether, dere diry, i been so busy, is i am farther ahead reeding then they think. I even red some of the Anthro book & *unnderstood.* i'm not teling enybody but you, Diry, but i am going reed next terms books, at leest as much as i can. i think Jack woud like that.

Febuary 4, Tusday

The new samester has began. All i haf to do is set around talking to Sharon & Prof Boileau on tapes, & then rite a sertain amount evry day, wich is going to cut in on you, diry, but do not be hurt, on account of i will always save the *best* & the *speshul* for you. We have so many secrets now we can not stop with each other.

Febuary 6, Thursday

Well, its a crasy world. Here i am lerning to read with all my hart, & on the news back in Harlem, they have walked out on the scools, 360,000 mostly blacks, clayming segragashun. Sharon & Lily took me to see Mama Pope & she sayd Big Ron tole her Woody's okay. He missed jail by the skin of his teeth in Adlanta, she sayd, but is out & free for more mischef. i dont know if thats good or bad. i had Sharon & Lily to meet Mama, but i coud tell Mama dident like Lily. Mamas doing the same rong to me that Woody does, thinking ive gone Tom out here. Thot Mama Pope would know better. She's Tom, but hates thinking i woud go Tom. *I wont.* Speeking of scool, some hunky mayor in Alabama turned some black childern out of scool saying they was a 'fire hazard'. if enybody done that to me i think i'd dye – or turn into a fire hazard as soon as dark fell.

Cold. Eating Baby Ruths maks you warm, but also gives you pimpels.

Febuary 7, Friday

This morning Lary showed up with that look in his eye so we went to the practise room. i hiked up my blue shift. He asked me if i dident have any pantys except black any more, he liked me beter in white or hony, & i sayd no. He sayd why not, you growing up to be a slut alredy at your age? i said no, i wasent, but diry, i woud *not* tell Lary why i (& Jacky) am wering black pants. That is *our* secrete, not Larys. Well, it turned out he come to the practise room on acount of Castro turned the water off last nite at that base the U.S. of A. got down there in Cuba.

Guanamo, Diry. Larys forgot his musik lately. Use to be he woud bang away playing real new good sounds on the piano. i used to wach him geting worked up, compleately lost in them keys, like he was on a trip or at least high on grass, then he'd dam nere make it, & get that hard on, & hop over me (always wilted, tho) – but now the musiks always stuff he played before, & he comes over at me like he's blaming me for Castro, instead of helping him with his musik. unless somthing changes quik, Lary isent going to write *any* more musik, & as far as him popping his nuts, forget it.

Speeking of popping nuts, Prof Boileau come around the other nite about haf drunk, sayd his wife was pissed at him, so i let him, but true to my vow to make it pay, i made him promise to take me down to Big Rons for some grass from Russel, & he gimme some extra mony for it. i also sayd i needed a new cote. i think it is beter that he pay me when he fucks me, on acount of i dont enjoy it nere as much as him. we fucked out on the floor. i dident want to fuck in the cubbord where Jacks pichure is.

Febuary 9, Sunday

Seen the Beetles. First time in the U.S. of A. Felt like I wanted to pee while i watched them on Ed Sulivan. They are grate! On next Sun, too. Not like Coltrane or James Brown where they ooze the soul out of you, Beetles more like pulling your pants down in public.

Febuary 12, Wensday

i am 16 years old. Now that stepdaddy is ded, nobody knows my birthday, diry, except me & you & Mama Pope. I asked Lary if he seen the Beetles & he sayd no, they wont last.

Febuary 14, Friday

Dear Diary.

Just found out i speling your name rong all this time. i am sory, but dont take it to hart on account of speling is 1 of my week points. i have let you go a hole week. Sense i been lerning to read beter, i been scared to write in you, so many awful mistakes, so desided mabey for a wile if evry friday (Sacred friday) i some up what hapened for the week, that would be best. This week not much hapened. They passed a civil rites bill in Washingtown, D.C., but not all the way. It still has to go past the Senate. Pres. Jonson says those fokes who jump all over the guverment (like Woody) do more hurt then our *real* enamys, & to stop it. i woud like to ask Woody about that, on acount of Pres. Jonson says good things about making the negros free even if he is from texas. i sort of dig him, tho he will never take the place of Jack, of coarse.

Lary come in laffing one day hollering 'Hodj Vodj', wich means frendly hello – remember how Castro cut the water off? Well, the U.S. of A. cut the *dolars* off, *that'll* get Castro where the hair is short.

Valantines Day. *You* are my Valantine, Diary.

Febuary 17, Monday

Beetles was grate! i asked Lary today if he seen them & he sayd no, but he read me a thing in the Times wich i am pasting in here:

Nothing is as ineptly talentless as the Beatles

Lary says he agrees, which means neether Lary nor the guy at the Times thinks they are any good & will go enywhere. He should know, hes a perfesser. Other one i like along with Beatles not counting Coltrane and James Brown is Aretha Franklyn, whose gone real cool & Peter Paul & Mary, favrite.

Febuary 21, Friday

Scool o.k, but the Indians of Calif & America very dull. i woud rather be lerning about the negros. But i got to hand it to Prof Boileau. He knows a hell of a lot about indians. i woud like getting fucked better by him now, becase i see he's so smart. I can read the book a litel now, but awful slow going.

Mama Pope says Woody left the South for New York to cool it. Glad to hear that. Sharon took me to the osean again. Lily didnt go so i got to ride in front. Sharons car is a MG. it smelt funy, like new lether & fresh. Sharon says all new cars smell that way. I gess i never been in a new car before. Sharons daddy gets her a new car for Crismas evry year, to keep her safe. Sharon is *reelly* rich, not jest rich. She got kicked out of 2 scools before this, but Prof Boileau sayd she was basically smart (like me) so got them to let her try here unnerneath of him even tho her grades bad. He give her 2 A's last term, so i gess she will stay in scool this time.

She has a unkle who is a famous Senater. i asked her if her unkle knowed Senater Gold Water. She sayd yes, & then made a sound like throwing up. i told her Mama Pope says Gold Waters going run agaynst Johnson next time & Sharon sayd not a chance.

Still taking tests but they are going slow. i am tired of DANSE & RYTHM, the same old crap this time as last, & i got to take *2 yrs* of P.E. ug! (state law) i woud rather take Miss Lench (my teecher in DANSE & RYTHM) down to the Hole-a-go-go & let the floorman take her on. Then *she* woud lern somthing.

Washed my hare to get the osean salt out, & up in curlers. Hope it stays *strait* for a wile!

Febuary 29, Saterday

Gess what! this is leep year, so i had to write a note to you, diary, on this speshal date wich wont hapen again for 4 years, when i will be 20 by then. When i am 20 i will look back at this day & remember all about it. 16 yrs old, doing good in scool. (flowing today) Have some good frends (Sharon). What hapened this week? Cassius Clay beet Sonny Liston in figting. Sharon says Cassius is her favrite, & Diary, he's sure a doll of a man. A good man, too. Back east they turned the dogs & the fire hoses on some black students who set around in circles clayming ecwality. They tossed 30 in the cooler. This hasent never hapened in L.A.

Mama Pope says she herd from Big Ron that Woodys with Malcom X again. Trubble brewing there. I give Sharon some of my grass for being nise & taking me for rides. We split a joint in my closet. She sayd be sure & keep it ditched, you can get 5 years in the cooler for jest having it. Dont i know *that*. Luky thing is, the Man geting scared coming down in Watts latly, they arent busting people so often down there for grass. But out here at the colege is somthing else. Theyre running scared. But there daddys can usally get them off.

Lary had me to sing some songs for Musik 309 today. i done 2 daddy taugt me, Bound No'th Blues, & Get Up Blues, & then one Woody likes to sing Scorned – 'i bene buked & scorned. . . .' Sharon plays the gitar & sings songs by Joan Byez & Bob Dylon like 'The Times They Are a Changing'. She has a real squeeky voice but kind of sweet & *perfeck* tone. She is 19 & lives in the dorms. Next year i can live in the dorms, Prof Boileau sayd. By then i will be legal with reel grades in college (all A's, Mabey) & can get hired as a legal student helper for my work in the lab. i can put down Mama Pope as the one who they suposed to call if anything hapens, but Prof Boileau say him & Larys name can go on the card too so nobody ever calls Mama Pope. Then the year after that i'll turn 18 & can do anything i want, so long as i got the mony for it. They have all these rules on acount of the moms & dads of rich kids like Sharon want to know for sure there girls aint geting jugged & drunk & blowing there heds on grass when they leave home. i dont know what difrence it makes wether it hapens at 16 or 18 – or 12, the way with me – unless you have babys. Sharon takes a pill so she wont. them pills cost a lot, & dont keep you from geting the sif & the clap like rubbers do wen they work rite. i woudent want to get fucked without a rubber, but thats sharons bisness.

March 9, Sunday

Dear Diary, i am geting very woryed about Woody. tonite on TV it had where Malcom X spliting with Muhamed. This is very bad. Rex who used to live with Mama Pope was a high up Black Muslim & he had a verry bad mouth, & when Malcom X splits, hes heded for trubble for sure. Thats why Mama Pope told Rex to get out. She dont like cutting peeple up & *nether do i*! Malcom Xs gon form his own black party. The TV says hes going to change the negros from non-vilence to vilence all over the cuntry. & *Woodys There*! wish he woud come home & stay here

---

March 13, Friday

Well, here it is Friday the 13th, Diary, & i havent got a thing to greeve unless Woodys in trubble & i dont know about. I gess Mama Pope is losing her touch with the Krystal Ball. They had a elecshun back east & Gold Water come in 3rd for republacin presadent. Loge was first, & he wasent even listed, they had to writ his name in. Sharon says Mama Pope had beter get a new kristal ball if she thinks Gold Water gon get to run agaynst LBJ.

Back east in New York 3000 blacks marched the capitol in freezing cold. i wonder if Woody was there. He beter had some overshoes, if he was. (wish i had a desent cote, but winter nerely over now)

Another friday come & gone in memry of dear Jack who i am still wearing black for. In ANTHRO 306 & 307 i dont know who had it wurst against the whites, the indian or the negro. The indian sure had it bad. First come the guns to kill him & then the pox, & the ones that lived thru guns & pox got struck down by liquer. Theyre beyond hope now.

Prof Boileau lemme write a exam in ANTHRO 306 yesterday. He sayd i dident quite flunk it. That is the furst colege test i ever passed, except Danse & Rythm. He sayd my writting is geting beter. i take notes when he lecshures like the other students do now, but he still wont let me talk in class. i woud be too skared anyhow. Bought some clothes at Orbacks today. Yellow shoes with cuban heels (11.95) to mach my button-down-the-front dress, 2 prs nylons (2.25) & 2 prs black pantys (3.00), new hony brasere (1.75), new garter belt (1.99) & a pale green orlon pleeted skirt looks good with my turquoize sweater *or* my new yellow shoes (8.99). Skirts is getting higher wich is okay with me, i am geting fatter & my legs getting look prety good. Lily took me shoping with her, but when we go out she treets me like im in the museum. She trys to be nise but i get sick of lily. She isent near so rich as Sharon. Lilys fokes live in town. She invited me over but i dont want to be a show nigger for lily. i told her Prof Boileau sayd i coudent go. Have a rash in my crotch. Tryed Nockzema, but it only burned worse.

March 15, Sunday

Jest to let you know, diary, thay sentensed Jack Ruby to death yesterday in Dalas. i thougt i woud care more then i do. i dont care what thay do with him, i jest dont want to here about him agayn. Still have a bad rash, beter tell Prof Boileau about it, but embarassed to. Vasalene seems to help some, but not much.

March 21, Saterday

i had this rash nearly 2 weeks now & its worse, its down my legs now some & iches when i wear nylons. Hope it isent from them black panties in honor of Jack. Lily sayd she notised i been swinging my ass lately so i tole her why, trying to walk without my legs shoud rub. She sayd i beter tell Prof Boileau. i will on Mon. Cassius Clay flunked his tests for the army. i jest cant hardly beleeve hes that dumb, he looks so smart & he moves so quik.

March 24, Tusday

Told Prof Boileau i had a rash & had to get somthing for it. He give me a tube of white stuff & it feels beter already. He had the tube rite in his office. Turned out he had the same rash, but never had it before i started playing with him, but *he* had it before, he sayd (he give it to me, i think.) He sayd its nothing bad & will go away. *Thank god – & thank Jack* – it wasent the clap. i havent never had the clap & *dont want it*. All these days i been thinking i probly had the clap & even skared to tell you, Diary. What a releef!

Watched TV tonite, jest goofed off. Geting tired of reeding, reeding, reeding. School can sure be a drag, i dont know how peeple stand it year after year. Sharon feels the same, but says its worse to drop out than stay in, she tryed both. Watched Stagecoch West, Redigo, Surfside 6 & The News. Man, the indians on TV sure isent like the ones we're studing in ANTHRO 306 & 307. The reel indians mostly jest set around trying keep out of the wind, & when the fleas & crabs got too bad they moved the whole town somplace else. Some of them even washed there hair in piss. i herd Mama Pope say that was good, once, but never beleeved her till now. Mabey i'll try it – might straiten it some, indians all have strait hair.

On the news the KKK sayd theyre going to start there own white towns. Good. They're sure kicking up a fuss down in florida. Some pore black woman got shot down & killed from a car, so some blacks strung a whitey up & give him the razor. 200 started rioting & the cops had to move in. Pore dead woman, & she isent the first or last. There was them 3 girls got chain whipped last month. Where does Woody get off saying the wemen isent in it?

March 27, Friday

i coud be going out tonite with a boy but Prof Boileau sayd no. His nayme is Charles. He is in my MUSIK 309 class. He sets beside me, which makes Lary pissed off. i tole Charles not to, if he wanted to get a good grade. Hes just a kid. i reely cant stand them red pimpels all over his fayce, but he means o.k. i think mabey he reely wants to take me out, & not jest fuck me.

But insted i am watching TV while Prof Boileau & Lary home with there wives. That riot at Jacksonville turned into 260 in the cooler. Theres stuff evry day on the news about the senate talking about cival rights & thats all, jest talk. Some woman named Kitty Genovese got stabbed & killed while 37 persons stood around watching in NY & nobody called the Man. It hapened Fri. the 13th. Diary, i think theres something in Friday. First Jack, then i got to move out of Larys practise room Fri the 13th. it was Fridy Lary & Prof Boileau had there first argument over me (signing up for classes). Now that poor woman Kitty dead on Fri the 13th. But more than that, i can feel a surge on Fridays that tells me its Friday, even if i don't know it. Mama Pope says the same, but her days not Friday, its some other day not having do with weeks, but the way the stars & moon work on her. Sometimes she chants out in back Nigger, Nigger, Never Dye, Black Skin & Shiny Eye, up to the full moon. She always plants her sweet peas & greens by the moon, too. Maybe *my* skittery has to do with the moon on account of im flowing, started this morning. i always get skittery when that hapens. A big erthquake in Alaska today. This is called Good Friday. Prof Boileau says they going start making movys of me prety soon. Mabey i will be a movy star after all, diary.

April 17, Friday

Dear Diary. No, i havent forgot you. Here it is Apr. 17 & the last time i writ in you was 3 wks. back. But what a cool 3 wks. Things clozed down here Easter & Woody come back so i stayed with him not only for Easter week but cleen thru the next, then he went back east last sunday so i come here & now its Friday again, & time to say hello to you, my close frend & pal.

Woody & me stayed over the Hole-a-go-go. He looks good, but he lost some wayte back with Malcom X who plans to go to Arabia to get a new name, on acount of he dosent want *nothing* to do with the whites or the Christans or, of coarse, the jews, so he is droping the names Malcom & X & gon take a name from the Ayrabs. Mama Pope says they all gon end up in hell for it, & Rev Smith dosent hardly talk to them any more, but Woody got Big Ron & Beverly & Leona & all them other cats thinking jest like him.

i think Woody is a super cool cat, Diary, & we had a good time for 2 wks, as you can amagine. i love it when Woody fucks me. He can turn me on quiker & beter then anybody & he says he loves me the best, but i know Woodys got wemen back east & all around & probly says that to them, too. But mabey he dosent. i sure love Woody. He looks better skinnyer. He says chasing around after Malcom X makes him skinny, Malcom X such a driver. Malcom Xs gon to Mekka wich is the most sacred place for Muslems, to find out where to take the blacks from here on, but Mama Pope says Malcom Xs doomed to take the blacks noplace, & Woody got mad. Woody gets mad quiker then he use to. He use to jest cool it in front of the Man & evrybody else, but now hes getting cocky & Mama Pope says hes going get cut down to size if he isent careful, but he tells her she just an old down-home nigger, & thats the dif. Nobody gon mess *him* up, he says. Mama Pope says there gon be lots of blood shed this summer (i jest hope & pray for Woodys safty, & *you do too*, diary, in the powerful spirit of Jack).

Woody tole Mama Pope – *i* know that, & i dont need your Kristal Ball, Mama, i can tell you *exackly* where the bloods going to fall. Then he says Mary Land where the skools been shut to black childern ever since 5 years, & then he says the N.Y. subways aint exackly gon be a picknick ground, & Florada & Alabama & Gorgia going get *there* blood let some, too, before the snow falls.

i asked Woody how come he knowed & he tole me he had 2 kristal balls, becaus he was a man, the left 1 & the rite 1, & Mama Pope onely had 1. But he coudent get her laffing, they both very up tite. Mama tryed Rev Smith to talk Woody out of his ideas, but Woody sayd the foney white Cristians who has no more love in there harts today than the ones who first brung us over has put the lye to Jesus, he sayd Jesus for blacks is a lame, as faded as them pictures in Rev Smiths church window, where they use to be full of pretty purple, red, blue & yellow Jesus casting seeds & lifting sinners, but now you hardly see Jesus or whats around him *compleatly* gone. Fly specks, too. Mama felt such misry to hear Woody talk I took her in my arms. The way she sobs, you dont hear a sound. No tears. Her skinny belly just jerks quiet like she got the heaves inside but not the heaves, theyre deep down misry trying to get out.

Rev Smith knows Woodys rite, he gets tong-tyed wich is somthing preachers never shoud, if theyre preachers. & its true about the faded pictures pasted in his store front church. They been in the sun to long.

Big Ron wants to go back with Woody where the actions to be, but Woody says Ron has to stay here to Take Care of Bisness TCB. Not too much longer theres going be action rite here in town. Woody seems to know. i never seen him act or talk like this before.

But when we're alone, Woody acts the same he use to. He tole me this was war, & the gratest thing ever hapened to the US of A, & that persons like Rev Smith still talking about intagrashun is out of it. Woody dont want intragrashun becase the whites isent *good* enuff. i wasent going tell him about Lary not getting a hard on, but i did. Woody jest about split a gut. But then later he got sober, & we had some reely cool grass that must of cost him plenty & after *3* joynts he tole me he seen Love unnerneath all this cival war. You know, Diary, Woody cries. We layed there with this cool high & fucked some & hugged each other & i sung some & Woody said he been thinking about me all this time, which i dont reely beleeve but its so good he says it, anyhow, & how coming to L.A. help heels him for going back to War. Musik from the Hole-a-go-go downstairs like to rattle the bed apart while we laid there in this high, with Woody wispering in my ear & giving me his tong. The place full of customers downstairs & we in a cloud. We spent the 2 wks like this, & having meetings. Woody let me go evrywheres with him, except with some men from the east, when i stayed with Mama Pope & wached TV.

Mama Pope says they going pass a law in Washingtown D.C. that'll help us all, but when i asked Woody he sayd them mothers been arguing it for 3 months now & when it *do* pass, it'll be no good & thayd have to do more than that to stop the War. He says any time that mother, Gorge C. Walas of Gorgia can get ¼ of the votes from a state up north in an election, it means War to the deth, no mater how meny white preechers throw thereselves in protest in front of a tracter like that one dyed in Cleveland.

He says its War when the Uncle Toms try to stop the blacks back east from jamming the worlds fare, or leeving there facets on to waste water & other disobediance.

He says when Humfry says that braking the law only backlashes on the blacks, that meens War, on acount of braking the laws the onely thing that brung any notice, ever, in a hunderd yeers of depression.

He says when some white son of a bitch can kill Medgar Evers in Jackson & get off with a hung up jury for murder, that means War.

He says when the L.A. cops can push us around like they do, with rasist Cheif Parker in charge, that means War, too.

Woodys lovely when he gets started. He had me not knowing where I was at, jest heering his voice & hating to come bak to colege. But he tole me to. He said, get your gut & your pussy & your brayne full of all this white supremecy shit. If it *takes* on you, i dont want you anyhow, but if it dont, you come back & we'll use it all *agaynst* them.

Mama Pope says this whole things going to blow over & someday peeple will wonder what all the fuss about, but when i'm with Woody i feel good. Jack unnerstans.

After Woody left i stayed with Mama. She talked old times, how her daddy & momma picked berys to stay alive & hugged to keep from freezing on to texas & how lucky they felt to get sleep sometimes on cottonseed in a whitemans barn. Where they setteled, they propped trees together for a house, & tamed wild cows & hogs for food. Shes so *prowd* of that! I think its sick. They shoud of stole & stole & stole. I rubbed her back with mustard for a long time. The skin on her backs as yong as a girls. My hands still smell hot from it. Good nite, Diary. Good Nite, Jack. Pray for Woodys sole & mind & Hart.

May 6, Wensday

Seen a movy called Lord of the Flys with Sharon. She liked it but i dident. About some boys who started living on a iland & ended up killing each other.

Took a test in ANTHRO & got a reel 'D'. i am honest-&-trully passing tests in Larys coarse, too. i am going to *stay in* colege. Prof Boileau been taking movys of me latly but Diary, dont get your hopes up, i am not going to be a movy star, it is jest pictures of me saying sertain sounds, which i say difrent from Sharon & Lily & them others. Thay sound the same to me, but i know Woody & Leona & Mama Pope talk black talk & i gess i done the same, but am changing now. They want the pictures of me so thay can make a movy showing how i made the black sounds, and how i had more amaganashun before i started writting & talking white. Compared to what Woodys doing, this dont seem like much.

Diary, i think its better to write in you jest once in a while. i coud put a litel somthing in each day, i supose, but what it be? About my pimpels? How many Baby Ruths i eat? That my period come late this month & had me wondering about nocked up? That i seen 3 movys (Elvas Presley called Fun in Acapolka (ug) & Rock Hudson in Mans Favrite Sport, along with the flys)? That i am studing my fool head off & can actally reed the books now?

Going to college is like quit living. Prof Boileau still wont let me go out with pimply Charley or anybody else in school, which is jest as fine with me, but i am geting sick of my closet. Here it is into May. One more month & scool will be over. Prof Boileau says im going to sumer scool, wich wont be so bad becase we get to go away to dig for ruins once in a wile. Meenwhile, what about Woody? Senater Gold Water is fighting the Cival Rites bill to the deth, & most peeple say he wont be presadent for the republacans, but Mama Pope says she still rigt.

May 22, Friday

Friday agayn. Doing beter in ANTHRO & MUSIK & Miss Lench in P.E. asked me to danse for the class last week so will probly get another A there. Have saved almost 100$ from what i get payd for lab work, bougt some cool clothes. Lily took me. Got new turquoize strech pants & a *boss* black & purple striped shirt, a pair of blue skuffs, a fluffy knit purple sweater (on sale, 6.99), 3 prs nylons, a new braserre (elastic all gone on both my old ones) & a pair of lether sandals from italy. Lary & Prof Boileau says mabey i can move to the dorms this sumer but we mite go on a long feild trip insted to dig.

Woodys at it agayn in Mary Land, they had to call the Gard out with there bayonets to get 1200 off the street when Guv. Wallas talked. Bet Woody leeding them. Hope so. But the march dident help much, Guv. Wallas got 1 out of evry 2 Mary

Land vote which shows how much the north thinks about the blacks after all. Diary, i take it back, i like Malcom X after all. Havent herd of him back from Arabia. The jews & the blacks fighting in Harlem, the jews drive aroun in cars with radios & guns. Havent seen Lary much exsept in MUSIK 309 latly, but he come around this week with that look, so we had our first practise in a long time (I used to think it was like tail-all-cozy, but its Talal Kozni, wich means 'hiding out to make love'. He finely explayned it.) He dont hardly play the piano at all any more, i think he jest likes to look at me once in a wile for old times sake & call me his 'kidress'. i am geting sick of it & dont see why i have to let him take my clothes off any more, sence it dosent help his musick, exsept he promised to give me a 'A' so gess i beter do it a while longer, it dosent hurt enything & Lary been desent with me all the time.

May 30, Saturday

This been a terable week. i think mabey Woodys in troubble, i felt it yesterdy, i was in ANTHRO & all of a suden felt a tug around my waste like Woody grabing me but geting pulled off by the Man. Where is he? i'll bet in jayle someplace. Thay realy tore things up in Mary Land. Whites throwed rocks & the Gard fired tear gas. Then them jews in N.Y. at it agayne with there vigalantes & the blacks in Harlem taking fighting lessons from the japs called Karate, evrybody geting redy for war. & Lary sick to deth from it all Thursday, practicly draged me over to the practise room & actaly got a hard on, but dident last long enuff to get in (& i was flowing, too, with a rag on, but that dident slow him down, he was that worked up!)

June 2, Tusday

Poor Teddy Kenedy, his wife lost a baby thay was having. Cheef Parker been sick, but hes back on the job. To bad it coudent been the other way around.

June 7, Sunday

Final tests start tomorow. 1 hole year! imagine, diary, a hole year of colege wich i done in memry of Jack, but will i be glad to get out of here for a while! its awful hard doing finals when so much going on in America. Not like the Indians had it. They could go years & years & never see a enamy, till the whites come, but now, enamys all over. They tryed to stop Gold Water at some guvs. meeting back in Cleveland, but it looks like Mama Pope is rite. Sharon says she cant even *think* about final tests, all this warring going on & her uncle in the senate fighting Gold Water & them red neck senators who fighting the cival rites bill to deth. You'd think it woud of been passed by now – seems like they been talking about it ever sence poor Jack dyed, but theyre still talking. Prof Boileau said i can take the final test in both ANTHRO coarses & he will grade me honest. if i pass he will give me 'A' & if i flunk he will give me 'B'. *i will not flunk*!!! Same with Larys, wich i am sure to pass, & A in DANSE & RYTHM. Terrable things all over, killings & knife fights in the subways & down south. i think i will quit watching the news, but Sharon sayd no, we got to change the U.S. of A. for the better, not ignore it. i told her about Woody some, & she wants to meat him, but i dont think that would be a good idea. Sharon woud be the very type to try & get Woody to fuck her for sosial action to show theyre equal, & i dont care how black Woody is, he probly woud if Sharon wanted, becase he *is* color struck no mater what he says.

June 14, Sunday

Diary, this has been a reely cool week! i passed both ANTHROS, got a D in Indians in America (hense a A), & a C! in Indians in Calif. (hense a A)! & i passed Musik & Lary will give me a A in Indapendant Study so i get all A's agayn, but *this* time, i reely & truly *past* something besides DANSE & RYTHM. i am reely so hapy. it is *good*. i think even Woody woud like it, Poor Woody, beeting his poor braynes out on the riots & marches & cival rites. i love him, but he works *so* hard & what does he get. Throwed in jail & tear gas in his eyes. But not this week, they finely got them Southern Senaters & Gold Water to stop talking in Washingtown, they voted to stop them, 71–29, which is the first time it ever happened, i gess, so it looks like theyll vote cival rites after all.

Lary asked me if i was for the rites bill, so you should of seen me do a Uncle Tom, Diary, i told Lary jest what he wanted to here, about how eqwal the U.S. of A. treeted evrybody, & how Mama Pope lived with the roaches in Watts & ate saltback because she *wanted* to. Lary hugged me, & i got them A's for sure! Diary, you dont know how good it is to have scool over, till you been in it for *hole year*!!! i'm sorry to say Bob Kenedy was going to run for Senater from N.Y. but defanately desided not.

September 1, Tuesday

September.

Am at Mama Popes.

Just come back from a summer that i thought was so good i coudent hardly wait to tell you, Diary. In fact, it was so good many times i wished i had you along to write about it, but stored you in a cubbord in the lab insted, for safty. But when i got back here to Mama Popes a couple weeks ago there was this letter from Woody that took the fun out of the whole summer & makes me wonder whether i better not just quit the whole college thing & go be with Woody – if he'll have me, that is. The way he sounds now, he doesnt care if he ever sees me again. i am wetting your pages with my tears, & they are real tears, not foney ones.

Well, Diary, i was going to tell you all about how we went to New Mexico, Prof. Boileau & Lily & Sharon & me & about 20 others stayed out on the desert digging indian ruins most the summer, & how i seen the Beatles here week before last at the Holywood Bowl, but i just cant get turned on to it, it all seams so *dum* after Woodys letter.

For 1 think, i missed him only by 2 days here in L.A. i got back the 17th of august & he left the 15th. God knows where he is now, & i woud do anything to see him & show him i *do* love him, i woud kiss his black ass or suck him off or whatever he wanted, i would do *anything* to darling Woody if i coud make him understan that i love him & havent got White like he claims. Dam it to hell, i wish i never woud of gone to New Mexco. What does it mean, digging up the ruins of a bunch of ded indians, compeered to what Woodys doing? Just like he says, i am so *sick* at hart i havent been able to face you, Diary, for the 2 weeks since i been back, but now Mama Popes tired of having me here in her little alley shack, i feel penned in, the foul brown smog makes me cry, Watts is just one big junkyard of people with flat tires at the curbs, busted hedlights, all the gas stations closed & gone broke, *why do we sit in a graveyard car whose engine wont start*? And i'm tired of TV, & even Big Ron & Leona & Beverly all gone east or someplace till fall for cival rights, & school dont start till 3 weeks (*if* i ever go back) so am writing my sad & lonly hart out to you, like i did so meny times before, & hoping you hear me & will give me the power to go on, you who are the soul & the spirit of Jack. Oh, Jack! If you was here, woud we have the misrys thats on us now today? No, i cant beleeve so.

Here is Woodys letter i am pasting in.

Aug. 14, 1964

Dear Trixie Mae

I waited 2 days past what I should alreddy, hoping you would get back from where Mama Pope said you were studying old indians. I hope you had a good summer in amongst the ruins of a lost race, under the thumb & giudance of your white masters. You better have had a good summer to justafy what you missed for your race, and for your Woody.

Trixie, you are 16 yres old now, and old enough for me to tell you some things that people like Rev Smith in his storefront church and faded jesus is scared to, and Mama Popes mind going more and more down home to texas too old to. They have to do with what we talked about so much last time I was out to the coast, or dont you remember those good times we had geting high and making love and you telling me how you beleeved in me, and me beleeving what you said was true. Then this summer I had a chanst – took the chanst – to get out to the Coast for a couple of days, mainly to see you, but you gone on what you told Mama Pope was the best thing every happened to you. Out on a desert half way between noplace digging up old bones while the fires of life flamed up around you in evry city in the U.S.A. Trixie, you are a good body, a good screw, a bright kid, but its time you growed up into the facts of your life. Mabe this letter will help.

About the time you and your professer friends took off for the desert (and the past) some black citizens down in Florida tried to take a swim in the ocean and got whipped by some whites. We rioted, and the governor of Florida slapped a ban on night marches. But we marched anyhow and they backed down. At this same time them 3 rights workers from the north turned up missing in Mississippi, the ones they just found dead last week. While you was out digging for old bones, the F.B.I. dug up the dam and found them 3 poor boys, and now you think the killers will get whats due? Well, Trixie, your old enough to know southern justice better than that.

The last time Mama Pope seen you, you was all steamed

up over that haf-assed civil rights bill the congres finely passed, and blue on account of Teddy K. in that plane wreck. Child, you're greeving and joying over the wrong things. Where was you when the 200 marched on the justice dept. in Washington? And unless you think all this happens far from your home, where was you when, while they dragging the river for those 3 boys, your dear old Cheif Parker slapped on a new law against the newspapers talking to Prisoners? I bet you wouldnt of read it even if you been in L.A. at the time. All Cheif Parker wants, Trixie, is to get it so he can *arrest* you and *not* say why. The newspapers hasent been much out there, but at least they spread the word when people like Big Ron and the others get busted by Parkers boys. Now they want to even take that away.

Trixie, I seen plenty white boys and girls in the south this summer while you scratching in that desert. But I didnt see you when Eliza Muhammed talked to 7500 black people in New York toward the end of June, or working with the folks in SNCC. And I suppose you missed what Mister Charley done in Virginia, to get around the new school law, voting in money for parents so they could send their white little mothers to a private school and let the blacks rot in a no-count free school with no money for the teachers. You didnt happen to see Lester Maddox wave his pistol and junior his axe handle, did you, when he drove out the blacks at his restraunt? hes a man to watch. Or when they mobbed the blacks on the fourth of july while that mother Wallace talked his dirty racist head off?

Ron showed me a real laugher when I got here to L.A., he saved it out of the Times, this here local yokel, Sam Yorty, who got so many blacks buffaloed he like to stay mayor the rest of his life, just on black votes, say we got the best 'race relations' in the U.S. and then in the same breath says there no police brutality here. Well, next time you see Sam, you tell him for me we got some plans for him and his hunky fuzz. The real tipoff about Yorty and his prince charming, Cheif Parker, come right after Yorty popped off about how good things are. You was too busy out with the diggers, so you coudnt of seen it, but Trixie, your a big girl now, and can read good and all, I want to tell you what Cheif Parker says, and let you think about this the next time you go off on a bone-hunt for dead indians. He says the *army* ought to handle the movement, not the police. He calls it a *revolution,* and one with blood, one 30 yrs old and likely to last another 30. Well, you got to admit Parker isnt a dumbell, but with a mind like that, where does that leave you and Mama Pope if the Man decides to come and get *you* next? Tell that to your dead indians, the next time you dig one up.

It's been a hot summer. Just in case you missed it, they had to call out a thousand troopers in Rochester. Tonight, while I'm writing this, the TV full of stories from down home where the whites and blacks alike marching for *your* civil rights is getting it through the head and in the gut with Mister Charleys guns and clubs, like Lemual Penn got it in the face driving thru Georgia. Thats how the hunkies reacting to the civil rights law, and keep this letter, just in case you have a tendancy to forget.

I'm leaving for Philly and where next I dont know, but think this over, Trixie. I'm not talking in anger, but its time you started medatating about this like Leona and Beverly doing, instead of acting way out in another world like Mama Pope, and that pathetic Rev. Smith do, god help his poor lame hide. Your still a good body and allright kid, and I think your loyal, but remember, we got a *faith* to *keep*, and dont you ever get lulled into forgetting.

Your pal and friend

Woody

September 2, Wensday

Woody is right. He been right the hole time. But what can i do? Go back with him & get throwed in jail? Mama Pope says hes out on bail from Alabama now, & scared to go back till they get a lawyer for him. What can i do, ignorent & no skill i cant even get a job outside the lab that pays but $1 a hr & woudent give me any mony left over for Woody.

Mabey he wants me to start turning tricks & sending the take to SNCC, but i dont think so. i beter stay in school. i got 30 credats so far, all A's. i got 12 last fall, 12 last spring & 6 this sumer, 4 from Prof. Boileau on the field trip & 2 from Lary for taping some songs before i left in Musik 311. if i quit that now, theyre all lost down the sewer.

Mabey i felt so blue yesterdy on acount of i started flowing. Today i know Woodys right, but i'm right, too & dont feel so blue. Rev Smiths right too & Mama Pope. & Lary & Prof Boileau, i dont know about Cheif Parker & The Mayor, but i bet Jacks soul, when it prays, prays for evrybody, even Cheif Parker, Jack was so rich in his human kindness. But the papers & TVs so full of mean, it makes you sick. On the dessert i forgot all about it, scraching all day just to loosen a indian skull from the clay, but evrything Woody sayd hapened, all right. And more. The very night Leona & me went to the Beatles they rioted in Chicago & bombed some poor newspaper.

Does Jacky K. care? Shes still in morning (& so am i, but i had to get off it a few times in the dessert i had to wear cotton pantys, the nylons made me sweat & break out & i dident have any black cotton) – shes still in morning, but she seems to be making it okay in spite of her sorrow. She just got back from italy after a long time. Mabey in time for Bobby to say he'll run for Senator after all from N.Y.

Tonight on the news theyre at it in Philly, i supose Woodys right in the middle & 2 nites ago the Man had to stay out of a entire 125 blocks there, it got so out of hand. 150 got hurt, but i just cant hold my breth for Woody evry time, any more.

Diary; i will let you know *as soon as* i deside what to do. i can move in the dorms this year if i go back.

—or should I start marching for SNCC?

September 9, Wensday

Still at Mamas.

Some cat come around yesterday looking for me. He heard from Big Ron I was going back to colege & he wants to go to. Hes finished high school & evrything, a smart boy, went to Jefferson Hi and all with good grades. His name is Truman. Hes a nappy hared boy, wears glasses, & talks very quiet. He dont try to jive you, so i didnt jive him. He told me a bunch of them wants to go to college on campuses like ours espeshally where there isent hardly any colored. So he drove me out & i showed him the campus. He borowed his uncles car, who is going to help pay his way. Arent hardly any colored can stay out of the draft if theyre as healthy as Truman, so he wants to get in college & get defurred like all the gray boys do. i showed him the bildings & where you sign up. We run into Lary. Hes been looking for me to come back, he needed my 'help' on account of the commys got in our own goverment now, theyre the ones pushing cival rites, some senaters say, but i dident want to go practise with Lary, with Truman around. Truman seen all he wanted to anyhow. I like him. Lary promised to drive me back to Watts later. So Truman left & I stayed.

Lary is changed, or mabey im just seeing him difrent now. His flat top hair gives him a cop look (thats how they look when thay got there helmets off). Hes got a mean looking picture of some man he calls George on his piano now. Lary wanted to know why i dident come back to school the same time the feild trip bunch got back in August, was i leaving him?

i told him the dorms dident open till Sept. 25, & besides, i wanted a vacashun.

Then he pulled the same shit Woody pulled about me leaving him in the lerch, just when he needed some Talal Kozni & *knowed* he was ready to pop off, but i gone to the desert digging skulls, ect. ect. ect. What a drag. Lary had on a black shirt & pants, & in the practise room with his dark glasses & very white skin looked like a gost with no eyes & floating hed. I knowed it was Lary, i coud smell the cigars & brandy as usal so i dident get spooked, but he give me the creeps just the same. I had on my blue shift, which i wore with Truman in mind, not Lary. I know Larys still with his wife, on acount of he sayed him & her was going to hear Gold Water at Dodger Stadium last nite. He still has his gold ring on his right hand, but exsept for that, never menshuned her – or his music, for that matter.

i told him me & Leona heard the Beatles in Hollywood Bowl but he coud care less. All he wanted to talk about was the *good news* – 'Yo Hear' – about congress going after the reds down south. & he got a hardon over how some Natzis attackted some red college kids right in Washingtown. Wow.

Diary, I think Lary gets me in there just to have sombody whose got to lissen. He toke his pants off & mayd me strip, & then started yaking. Lary is turning into some kind of prevert, & i dont know whether to tell Prof. Boileau or not. i onely haf to take 2 more Music coarses underneath of Lary, so mabey i can stand it.

i am glad in a way this happened. Larys a kook, but it helps me see Woody, poor dear cat, hes kind of a kook too in his own way. What good is changing the goverment if your lifes recked doing it? Evrybodys turning into a sosial actionist & forgetting why else theyre on earth – to make music, to love & be kind. i think i trust Prof Boileau more than any now, but i think i'll ask Mama Pope to give me a reading, even if Woody thinks shes too old any more to know whats what. Shes still got her kristal ball, & it has ways of its own.

What do you think, Diary? Help me pray for giudence to the darling spirit of you-know-who, which is your spirit too.

Lary drove me home before supper. He's a wild driver.

September 27, Sunday

Back in school, & wonderfull news, Diary.

i have so much to tell you, but will make it short. i am in the *Dorm* with a room mate naymed Alice who is probly very nice but i havent seen yet on acount of she is late to school on a trip somewheres but can hardly wait. (maybe we can trade clothes if shes my size!) As i write this to you i am this very moment in my own dorm room! *No more closet & cubbord.* No more Mama Popes lumpy sofa except when i want. No more practise room, no more screwing Prof. Boileau at all hours, unless i feel like it. It is the best room you can imagine. Alice & me *each* get a bed. i have my own chester drawers & a desk. i cant have TV here but who wants it now i am a sofamore (all A's!) & so much studing to do? Besides we got TV downstairs if we want.

i had a long talk with Mama Pope after our reading the kristal, which is why i come back to college. She says its the rite thing on acount of my stars say im headed for woe unless i get persons around who are strong & powerful to take care of me.

i said who'd want to take care of me? & she said, i give these persons good cause to take care of me. She said my stars make me a fighter but a dreemer, & i got imaganashun for the future for other persons to groove on. She said Woody doesnt need me so much now as later on acount of Woodys headed for troubble later so i better cool it & stay free insted of getting in troubble *with* Woody, i coudent stop him anyhow.

She said she sees a powerful man in my future who's going to help me & i help him, & the man is white, not black.

So i said what about college & she looked in the ball like she does, with her cheeks sagging & them silver earings hanging into the light that comes from underneath of the ball & she said, 'Yes, yes, yes, go back. i see it clear!'

When she talks like that she starts panting & thats when i beleeve her. She panted from vision dreams ever since the first time i slept in her room after moma dyed. And after stepdaddy took me away and after he got knifed & they found me about starved out from waiting 3 days later, Mama *knew* all hed done to me. She wispered, 'your *my* yellow pumpkin now.' So i desided to go back to colege, but i said, 'Woody wont like this,' & she said, 'Woodys only a little *part* of your picture, child, i see the *big* picture tonite.' She layed down rite after. When dear Mama Pope reely sees something, it wears her out rite now. So i give her a nice mustard rub.

i still got my radio. I herd something to make Woody & Big Ron giggel at the Man. J. Egdar Hoover who is head of the FBI said the riots this summer wasent planned, they just hapened.

All the saroritys here signed a plege not to keep colored girls out. There arent any but me on campus anyhow, & i dident try to get in.

September 28, Monday

The sad report about dear Jacks deth is out. They claym Lee Ozwald done it all alone & the John Burchers & Commys hadent nothing to do with it.

September 30, Wensday

Signed up for coarses today. Same old stuff under Lary & Prof Boileau, but these the last with Lary (which i am just as glad of, as you know) & Prof Boileau promised next year i can take reel coarses from other teechers. *if* i work & my speling gets better. He sayd im talking prety good & will let me talk in class if i do my lessons as good as last time. And, Diary, i do have 1 reel coarse this time, Personal Hygene, which Prof Boileau says the easiest 1 in college & a good 1 to start on. Here they are:

ANTHRO	476	Feild Study	(4)	Prof B
MUSIK	432	Contemparary Techniks	(2)	Lary
MUSIK	399	Indapendant Study	(3)	Lary
HEALTH	120	Pers. Hyg.	(2)	???
P. E.	169	Danse & Rythm	(1)	(ug!)
			12	

Run into Truman in line. He says him & about 6 other cats are trying to get in. I better not see much of him till my writing gets better or he'll wonder *how i got here*. Hes bright, but no jive. Like.

October 1, Thursday

Alice showed up today. Diary, i dont know if i shoud tell you this thing, but Man, is she *fat*. Luckly she is also nice. She has 2 gygantic stufed animals, a hugh teddy bear & a python & she lets me keep the teddy bear on my bed. Sad to say she has terrable red pimpels all over her butt, probly from eating. i have to lauff when i think i thought we might trade clothes. i coud wear her bra for sholder pads!

October 2, Friday

A bunch of students up at Berkaly rioted. They hemmed in a cop car for hours. it had to do with them pushing cival rites on the campus. Alices last nayme is Gottschauk & has red hair. She woud be very pretty if she lost about 80 lbs.

October 3, Saturday

Smog! Sharon has a litel place of her own this year off campus, was there this afternoon. Groovy, with her own record player, a beatiful blue sofa that folds out to a bed in the living room, & seprate bedroom with 2 fancy white hedbords in gold trim. She is lucky.

October 5, Monday

You cant beleeve what i seen. Sharon took me to the county museum to see mamentoes from sweet J.F.K. Diary, i seen the very chair he used to rock in to ease the misry in his poor back. i seen the very desk where he signed all the wonderful things he did. The Kenedy fambly got the collection together & showing it around the U.S. of A. i dident even know about it but Sharon, bless her hart, knows how i feel about our fallen leader (still in morning for him) & so when she found out took me down. Alice coudent go. (She wonders why i always wear black panties, but wont tell her) She is too fat to fit in Sharons MG, even crossways in back. Poor Alice! She is majering in HOME EC & plays the chello. At the museum they woudent let you touch the chair, but i leened across the ribbon & did anyhow. i can still feel the smooth wood on my finger tips. *His* chair!

October 12, Monday

Not much new. Alice come back early last nite from the liberry while i was smoking a joint. (i got it from poor Russel whos dabbling in heroine, i think, but still pushes grass. Hope he dosent get strung out on that awful heroine.) Alice wanted to know what the smell was but i dident tell her. i gess i better not do it in the dorm. i told her it was a playne cigarette but i dont think she beleeved me. all i need is for her to blab. Am doing good in school, im not on grass much, but do like to get a high on Sundays when nobodys here & i can think about Woody when im high & i sure woud like to fuck him, my hare down there itches thinking about it.

Big Rons in troubble, theyre trying to bust him for some old charge that happened years ago when the Man raided the black muslems here, but Mama Pope thinks he'll get off, Ron says it isent as easy for the cops to bust you as it used to be before the courts got busy making them turn in good evadence. Hope so, though Ron says busts for traffic still way more for blacks than whites. TV had all about some white mothers setting down on acount of there lily white schools getting black childern down home. They make me so sick! Sharon wants me to get some pot for her from Russel, but i can just see her Uncle in the Senate raising Cain with me if i did that & she got caught. i never told her Russel pushing it. i gess she just figured it out. i sure like Sharon, but she will have to get her own pot from someplace else for a while. Or shoud i give her? sometimes, diary, i cant tell if i do things out of wiseness or plain meanness. Sharon deserves it if anybody does.

October 13, Tusday

Diary, i herd today darling Jacky K. is going to come to L.A. before Chrismas. i will see if Sharon can help me to meet her, since Sharons Unckle has met Jacky. i woud like to thank her for Jacks picture which i had over my desk till Alice made fun of it so i put it in my drawer, but look at it evry nite on acount of its next to my brush & comb. Alice says evrybody wants to make a hero out of Jack but he isent worthy of it. Well, sometimes i want to say screw Alice, all 250 lbs. of her ass. i woudent give 1 hare on dear Jacks head for *all* of Alice when she talks like that, but dident tell her that. She is in my MUSIC 432 & thinks Lary is keen. They woud make a good pair. Larys geting fat, too, like Alice.

October 15, Thursday

A very nise thing happened today, Diary, in the mist of all the shootings & marches & stonings & riots, Martin Luther King was give the Prize for Peace they give away in Sweden. Wow, you shoud of herd what them red neck Senators said in Congress about Dr. King & how he dident deserve it. (not Sharons Uncle Jules, he's liberal)

P.S. – i'm sorry calling alice a ass to you, diary. She is, but i shoudent call her that.

October 16, Friday

Friday. Just another week. Some poor prevert next to the presadent was canned. Got caught in a washroom. Boy, did that make Lary happy. Anything LBJ does wrong, Lary is for, because LBJ is too soft on Commys. Lary wanted to have a practise session over it to celabrate, but i sayd i had the curse (a lye). i wish somtimes he woud ask Alice instead, except youd haf to have a dick longer than Larys to reach into her past those *huge* legs. She realy ougt to reduce.

Red China has the A bomb now so i spose our days is numbered.

October 23, Friday

Not much new. Took a test in HEALTH 120 this week & got a B—, but nobody gets less than a C in HEALTH. They dont grade you on speling as much as other coarses. Diary, it has been 11 months since poor Jack dyed & you begun. The wind is blowing terrible today & rain perdicted. i am snuggeled down in my bed cozy & warm, happy for Rev King & his noble prize worth $53,000, which puts him on easy street. Alice went home for the week end (lives down in Orange County) so i am having a nice joint thinking about Woody & putting out of mind all the sad things. Gold Water says intagration is morally wrong, Teddy K. is still flat on his back from his plane wreck, & the cathlic guy in charge of L.A. has told all his preachers to shut up about Prop. 14. i gess i havent told you about Prop 14. it is a thing on the elecshun next month which if it passes, means black persons cant rent certain houses. Well, im in my cozy house tonite, in spite of the roaring cold wind on my pane & Prop 14. They are rioting in the N.Y. subways at this very hour, the radio says, but i am feeling too high to hear them. i want Woody here. i am feeling to wonderful lovely high to write in you any more, Diary, so good nite & dont get cold. i will sleep with you to keep you – Jack – warm.

October 29, Thursday

Sharon & Lily & me went to see President Johnson in town. Awful cold & windy. Wore my crummy old brown coat. i coudent see him very good, but got a good look at the verry car poor Jack was killed in. its about a mile long & black, with secret service men all over the bumpers. The reason i coudent see Johnson so good was they had a bullet proof glass bubble over it. Oh, how i wish they had it before! Sharon said they did, but Jack refused to wear it, did that man *want* to get hisself killed? I sure hope Johnson beats Goldwater next week. Alice bougt a pumpkin for our window. It stinks sweetly black from scorched candel. We put some old horn-rim glasses on it & cut gappy teeth to look like Goldwater. Ill be glad when votings over & the pumpkin threw out, because, diary, i will tell you a secret, I hate pumpkins from the time stepdaddy always called me Yellow Pumpkin when he got drunk. He had no call to taunt my skin. He called me Yellow Pumpkin the first night he done it to me, & from then on made sure i wore my drawers, so my dress dident get stuck up on my butt like it does with no drawers, he wanted me to hisself, i gess, at least for a while. Halloween is my *un*favritist time. Mama Pope calls me Yellow Pumpkin but she says it nice. Sometimes Alices sweat smells like stale pumpkin on the inside, i dont like that.

November 3, Tuesday

Late.

Stayed up to make sure Johnson won *for sure*. He not only won, he *clobbered* Goldwater. *ha ha* Alice is laying in her bed mad. I shoudent feel so good but i do. I supose Lary will want a

Talal Kozni tomorrow to get over Goldwater getting clobbered so bad. Well, it will be worth it, diary, to know Johnson got it. He promised to stop the war in Vietnam & that will save untold lives & he will keep fighting the KKK & other fascists. But, Diary, Prop 14 won too, by 2 to 1. Bobby won in N.Y. of coarse. Well, you win some & you lose some. Woodys back in N.Y. with Malcom X, Mama Pope says, but he'll be home around Chrismas. Sharon invited me home for Chrismas, isent that nice? Well, good night, Diary. Good Night, fat alice, i shoudent say this, but im glad you lost.

November 4, Wensday

Diary, i think Alice & Lary seeing each other. i figured poor Lary to call me for practise after Goldwater got clobbered, but dident. But old Alice looking funny at Lary in MUSIC 432 these days. i wonder ... Shes out at the liberary now ... or is she?

November 5, Thursday

That thing i was telling you about Alice. its *true*! Alice is such a big blabber mouth she cant keep any thing. She come back last night all hot & bothered, & coudent keep her mind off it.

'How long you knowed Lary?' she asked, & i said since last year. She said, 'you ever been in his practise room?' & i said, 'What do you mean?' & then she told me Lary got her down on her back & felt up her pants.

I said i dident beleeve it, profs dident do things like that, so she said, *feel*. Well, i dident want to feel Alice in the crotch, but she made me & her crotch was all wet. 'i only get wet like that when i come,' she said (shes *forever* diddling herself, I've knowed that ever since last month) & she said Lary made her come with his finger.

i said i still dident beleeve it, what did they talk about?

She said, 'you wont beleeve it, but about Goldwater losing the election.'

That convinced me, of course, Diary, on account of Alice isent bright enuff to make that up but i dident let her know. I asked her if Lary fucked her & she said no, he dident even try to take his 'thing' out. Man, is she turned on! i think she wanted to go around showing evrybody her wet pussy, but she shoudent of made me feel it. i think Alice dosent care who makes her come, as long as she comes. But to do it with a teacher is special. i wish Woody was here, im tired of hearing about how grate Larys finger is.

November 7, Saturday

Alice still talking about Lary. That suits me just fine, only i hope he dosent flunk me in my music now that she's taken over. He cant, of coarse, i have too much on him, though would hate to use it against him *or* Prof Boileau. Prof B. & Sharon are putting together the movy they took of me last spring. It is going to be called The Electric Child, which is me, who learned nearly evrything i knowed before colege from TV or radio or movys.

Diary, i will explan what i can about Prof Boileaus projeck. He says i am 100% tribal, which means, i dident find out about sputnik & John Glen for exsample from a book, I seen it on TV the same time evrybody else, just like all of us 1 big *tribe*; & i dident find out how Lincon freed the slaves (ha ha) from a histry book, I seen Gone With The Wind with the rest of the 'tribe'; & i dident find out about micky mouse reading comic books off alone, i use to watch micky mouse club on TV like evrybody else in 'the tribe' in difrent houses all over the cuntry, like Sharon up by Frisco & Alice down in Orange Country, & i dident read about poor Jack in the paper, alone, a week late like they did when Lincon dyed, i herd it on the radio with evrybody else about 2 minutes later, & Lee Ozwald killed in *plane site* for all the Tribe to see, TV makes it hapen like around 1 big campfire.

So, Prof B. says, since i lerned all these things *with evrybody else* insted of off alone someplace, i have had a 100% *tribal* experiance with evrybody in the whole U S of A, which Prof B calls the Electric Age & why i am called The Electric Child. If i had of went to school & berryed my nose in a book like the other kids here where the words take the place of real life, i woud not be 100% tribal, & i woud not be such a good case. These is Marshal Macloons ideas. You see, diary, what he wants to do now is *un*tribal me by college, reading, writing, & see how i end up. A mess, probly.

November 9, Monday

It turned out the reason Prop 14 won was the real estate persons from all over the U.S. of A. give money to Calif. for the campayn to stop fair housing. i wonder how LBJ can keep on saying the blacks got nothing to be vilent about? Alice says her daddy says they ought to lynch Warren who is cheif justice. i woud like to see her try, over my dead body. Alice is diddaling evry night like mad. She wants me to watch.

November 11, Wensday

Alice wanted me to diddle her last nite, & to lay on the bed, but i told her the bed woud brake. She hangs around Lary all the time and never studys. i'll bet her grades are going to hell. Mine arent. I got a lot of persons to show I am good enough for college, & will show them. Saw Truman in the caf today. He wanted to talk but I'm scared to talk in front of him yet. He's really smart. I want to get good so Prof. Boileau will know he did right to help me. The smarter I get the more I can help

Woody, too. Alice smells like stale butter. She farts in her sleep alot. The last thing i want to do is diddal *her*.

November 20, Friday

J. Edgar Hoover called Rev. King a liar, on account of Rev. King said the FBI wasent moving fast enough in the south. I beleeve Rev. King, but Alice beleeves Hoover. She said if i diddled her off just once, she'd take me home thanksgiving. NO thanks, i'll take Mama Pope a big goose & spend it with her, before going with Alice & her fancy house.

November 23, Monday

Well, Diary, you know what yesterday was, the *1st* annaversary of the death of the greatest American to fall since Abraham Lincon, John Fitzgerald Kennedy. Today i am wearing white panties for the first time Jackie & me (& many others in the world too, I suppose) have spent the year in morning & now a new dawn breaks. Jacky said on TV today 'My morning is over, but my heart has not heeled.'

How true!

Jacks grave afoot with millions all weekend, a prosession that never stopped through rain or sleet day or night. How i woud like to lay my wreath (my *self*!) at his grave to worship the remains of his dear body which now is spirit in heaven to guide us – you & me, diary – in the years ahead. All over the world people weep anew for our lost hero. Diary, *you* are 1 year old. How does it feel? I love you as much as the first day, & will until the day we part, which will not be till the day we dye – together.

November 24, Tusday

Alice out late with Lary & made me feel her when she got back. Wet again. The reason? Some CIA people tryed to bomb Havana. I gess that turned Lary on pretty good & he put in a call to Alice quick. Alice tells about Lary doing the same things he done with me, but claims he's getting hard ons. A new victim evry year, hey, Diary? His poor wife. Alice says Larys already promised her an A in MUSIC 432. Big deel. (I wonder what I'll get?)

November 29, Sunday

Dear Diary. I spent the weekend at Mama Popes. I took a huge frozen goose (12 lbs) down from Alpha Beta here, on account of you get better prices out here in the edge of town than you do in Watts, Sharon says. Anyhow, I have some money hid in my room where even snoopy Alice cant find (stuck underneeth the desk top which you got to take the drawer all the way out & reach up under to get) saved from my lab money, which is 1.75$ per hr. this year. (I have over 100$ there) So Sharon drove me to Alpha Beta on Tusday for the goose which had to thaw out all day Wensday in our closet to be ready for stuffing Wensday night. Alice claimed it smelled her clothes up, but I think the other way around.

Wensday night Big Ron picked me up & I stuffed the goose at Mama Popes with rice dressing, my favrite, mince bacon, onion, selery & spices. I used nutmeg instead of sage, it goes better with goose dripings. We cooked it in Leonas oven from early morning & brung it hot over to Mama, on account of she wont go anyplace any more, & I made goose gravy with lemon rind for season. Leona fixed the yams and vegtables & Ron (hes living with Leona now) bought the mince pies & we had a super dinner. Ron brung a pint from Thrifty Drug, too. We all crammed in Mamas around her oak table. She needs the springs fixed in her sofa, Leona & me sunk down so low our eyes practicly even with the plates. Mama in her red shawl creaked her rocker all dinner long, it keeps her misry down. I felt little agayn, so eyelevel at the table, while Mama prayed her head down with her silver earrings rocking jesus god for the greatest blessing in the world, life, & thank god for the blood in our bodys, the air we breath, the land we stand on, prepare us for our souls jorney thru this unfrendly world and receive us into Your loving home till the goose got cold & the gravy almost too thick to pour. I wanted Mama to stop praying to save the gravy, but Ron sayd with his eyes, let her rambel on. Her wallpapers all peeled. There use to be yellow daysies on it. Finely Leona dished up the yams & the smell of brown sugar brought Mama back. I love her. (Diary, she said the goose the best one she ever tasted, how that for prayse?)

Woody wasent there, but next best thing, he wrote a letter from N.Y. to us all. Strange news, Diary. Woodys changed his name from Woodrow to Ali Ki Bar. Now, dont laugh, i wanted to, too, when Ron read the letter, but its the truth. He says Cassius Clay going to change his name to Muhammud Ali for the Black Muslims, & Malcom X changed his to Malik A Shabazz, which is Ayrab. Woody's gone clean past the Black Muslims & SNCC to Malcom X's out fit, which is the organasation of Afro-American Unity. Thats why he went for something Ayrab like Ali Ki Bar, instead of a Muslim-type name like Woody X 75. Big Ron's about to change his, but he cant decide to what, & as soon as he changes his, Leona & Beverly will change theres. They said for Mama Pope to change hers, but it turned out nobody knows Mama's real front name any how, so she dont have to drop it at all. We tryed to get her to say where her name come from but she woudent. The Pope part comes from slave days, Ron said, & thats why we're all dumping ours & she ought to hers. Like Cassius Clay says, he dont want to be named after his grandaddys white master, he dont want the religon, the name, the nothing. Mama Pope says, 'Don't move too fast, you got to have something to move *to*, not just away from.'

Big Ron said, 'We do, now. We got Eliza Muhammad & Malcom X & Rev King. We're moving out, *now*.'

But you coudent get Mama Pope to smile. She said the sadness about to come on the world was more than she could bear. She said next year we woudent be having thanksgiving, we'd be grieving for Malcom X & all the others who gonna dye in blood.

I wonder.

Russel brung some really good grass, so after dinner we wached TV & all got high. Mama Pope, too. She loves pot, but cant afford it all the time. Russel's getting more & more strung out from dope, i think. He hardly ate anything, except the pie, for its sweetness. Ron & Leona took what was left of the goose home, except a little for Mama & me to nibble the weekend.

Woody says he will *definately* be home for Chrismas, & asked special about me. I asked Mama Pope if i shoud go with Sharon or stay for Woody, but she coudent tell, the kristal clouded. What do you think, Diary?

They say on the news tonite the FBI knows for sure who killed those 3 boys last summer & buryed them in the dam in Mississippi. Awful hot in the dorm tonite. Alice isent back yet, so the room still smells sweet in spite of the heat. Poor Alice sweats so much when its hot like this it runs down the inside her legs like big tears.

December 7, Monday

Sharon asked me agayn for sure to come home with her. I wish I knowed for sure if Woody's coming home. Sharon lives up in Montaray, wich is a very rich place. She showed me pictures of her house . . . Wow. Set in woods that look like big Chrismas trees, with a wide lawn going down to the osean. The house is 3 storys tall & looks like a cassel. I'm scared to go up there, *but must*, to follow Mama Popes word that i got to be nice to persons who *can do me good*, which means $$$$$. But Woody might never come home agayn (I keep fergetting to call him by his new name, *Ali Ki Bar*).

2 more wks. before vacation. I have past all my tests with at least a C – this term. (got 2 B's!) But not reelly & truley taking a full load. The Feild Study under Prof Boileau is just the lab stuff. He shows me pictures of hunderds of things & I tell him what Mama Pope calls them, & what other people in Watts like Big Ron or Russel call them, & what i call them, like for egsample a pancake (or hotcake), Mama calls it a hoe cake, or sometimes a paddy cake, & i heard Ritcherd the cook call it a flapjack, but like i say, its a pancake.

Mama's 'down home' talk, Ritcherds western nigger, i gess, more up to date, but the words keep changing. Prof Boileau says most the difrences gone, now with TV making evrybody in the 'tribe' talk the same. He says TV's making persons into 1 big U.S.A. where we all think the same & use the same words. Well, mabey so, Diary, but if we're 1 big tribe & with Chrismas coming up, you'd think we woudent act so mean to each other. They're still bombing black folks homes in the south, & the kids up at Berkaly rioting all over the place again. Meenwhile the NAACP trying to fight Prop 14, but its already passed & NAACP is late as usual. The doctors, theyre banding together to try & wreck Medacare for people like Mama Pope. Some *tribe*! At least they finely arrested the persons who killed them 3 boys last summer – 21 of them, some of them policemen. Wonder if they'll ever spend a day in jail? They're already out on bail.

December 9, Wensday

They dropped charges on 19 out of the 21. Southern Justice, just like Woody says. Fat Alice is really lording it over me. She knows how to say hello in Hungery. Hodj Vodj. Big deal. I pretended I never heard it. Lary invited her downtown when they opened a big fancy new place to play music in. Alice said Larys wife was sick so he took Alice. She wore her pink tafetta dress & pink heels. Her & Lary been going hot & heavy in the practise room. But that dosent satisfy her, she just come back here a few minutes ago & wanted me to diddle her, but I'm busy writing. I shoudent tell you this, Diary, but Alice finely made me sleep with her 2 nites ago. I think she's going to get kicked out of school, she never studys, she thinks about diddaling *all* the time, first with Lary then with me. I wonder what woud hapen if somebody real like Woody or even Prof. Boileau throwed a good fuck into her like people supposed to, instead of all this finger fuck. Anyhow I am ready to move out of the dorm if it keeps up. Lary never took me anywheres the whole time I helped him. Alice wants to kiss me with her tong but *I will not*. Let her do that with Lary through his dark glasses or his black pants, shes his Kidress now.

Well, vacation soon.

December 11, Friday

Saw Rev King get his Peace Prize on TV. Lovely!

December 14, Monday

Still cant decide on Sharon or Woody for Chrismas, & Sharon leaves this Fri. for home. Help me, Diary.

December 17, Thursday

Have to decide by tomorrow. No more word from Woody, I phoned Ron & Leona today. I know I ought to go with Sharon, but . . . what if Woody come home like last sumer & Im gone?

That woud be the end. Diary, what shall I do? If I knew for *sure* Woody coming home, I woud stay. ???? *Yes!* Here are the pro & cons:

WOODY	SHARON
ALL KI BAR	ATTWATER
BLACK	WHITE
MAN	WOMAN
MEAN	NICE
BIG YUMMY COCK	MG & FANCY HOUSE
HIGH ON GRASS	DRUNK ON DRINKS
COLORED PEOPLES TIME CPT	ON SKEDULE DAY & NITE
WATTS	MONTARAY
HOLE-A-GO-GO	A CASSELL ON THE OSEAN
BIG RON, RUSSEL ECT	SHARON HAS 2 BROTHERS, BOTH YOUNGER THEN ME
MAMA POPE	MIGHT MEET SHARONS FAMOUS UNCLE
SOME REALLY GOOD HIGHS WITH WOODY	ALONE IN BED, BRAN NEW SHEETS & A MAID! (SOUL SISTER, PROBLY)
NO MONY	MONY

There it is Diary, what woud you do? Everything comes in twos. Today Teddy K walked from his hospital bed where he laid for 6 months, but Nat King Cole got cancer. One for the other. I think that means I better go with Sharon if I know whats good for me, its the rich who always walk away from the wrecks.

December 18, Friday Night

Well, Sharon left without me. I think I made a big mistake but I stayed for Woody. Now if he dosent come back east I might as well dye. Dorms close for vacashun tomorrow. Diary, I am going take all my money & leave you in the drawer here. You will be lonesome, I know, but I will think of you, & will tell you all that happened. See you next year, sweet. Alices folks picked her up today to take her home. Nether 1 of them is fat. She wanted to stay here with Lary but coudent figure out how. I will tell you happy new years now, diary, & will see you soon. Keep remembering your spirits is Jacks & you will not be lonesome.

1965

January 3, Sun. Afternoon

Dear Diary. Sunday afternoon & most the girls not back yet, including Alice. I am on my bed with you. The wind blowing but not hard, & perfeckly clear. The campus nearly empty. You can hardly hear any sounds of traffic. Compared to Watts which is a flat junkyard & the wind from the Goodyears tire plant blows that sickly sweet all over, this is way out in the fresh air cuntry away from all earthly cares. Lonesome, except for you, Diary, & I dont know hardly where to begin. (The rose parade is over, & once again I am not the quean)

I will begin listing the things I own. First of all I went shopping after I wrote in you last, & now have:

— A new pale blue half-coat *with mouton collar*, plus old brown one (ready to make rags of)

— Shoes: 2 prs flats, 2 tennies & my old yellow ones, a new pair of black heels and 2 prs italian sandals which I mostly wear

— A new white jersey dress (*very* cool, with a roll neck, fits like a dream) with black belt; old blue shift; old yellow one

— Sweaters: old purple one & old turquoize one (need some)

— Some new underwear, bras, ect ect ect, wont list all

— My usal toiletry stuff, black & white creme, hair strait, wont list it all, but got some groovy french perfume from Leona for Chrismas

— Books, ect, worth about $75

— My old radio

— Picture of Jack, & you, Diary, which are getting so big I have you now in sevral tablets

— My jewlry, which is my garnet ring, my silver bracelets & ear rings, some new beads, & what Woody give me, a *gold* medalion for my neck with Arab writing on it (beautiful!)

— Cash: $14.61. That isent much but have a check do tomorrow for about $75.

— Old pink blouse, turquoise blouse, old olive green pleeted skirt

— Black & purple striped shirt, plus a new white one

— Pants: real old pink hip huggers, old turquoise stretch pants, the Levis i wore on the dig last summer (2 prs)

— Robe: old majenta one (need a new one)

— Niteys – 3, old baby doll blue, old white, new turquoize shorty, new candy stripe pj's, cotton, for cold weather.

— Boots – 1 pr white rubber for rain & the black wellingtons I bought for the dig

— Blue denim jacket from dig

— Old bushwacker hat from dig I wore to keep the sun off.

So you can see I am ready for the worst. And I got the *loan* of a whole flock of things – all the stuff in the lab, Alice's stuffed bear & python, & a lot of her junk she offered me, to do what I did with her last month, but plan not to, any more, which leads me to my vows for 1 9 6 5:

1 – quit everything with Alice. Finger fucking is for kids or old maids

2 – Move out as soon as possable from her as a room mate

3 – Not take any more MUSIC, try & make grades *on my own*

4 – Explayn to Sharon why I stayed here but still want to be friends with her & go to Montaray next chance

5 – Forget trying to figure out Woody (I will not call him by that other name even tho it means the end)

6 – Pray for Mama Pope who is getting old & weak

7 – I will be 17 next month, try & go on my own as soon as I can

8 – *Stay in school*
9 – Not fuck unless *I* really want to, or can get something good for it
10 – Never try heroine or cocaine like poor Russels doing now, never go on anything but pot, which includes liquer, unless I have to drink liquer to keep from embarassing somebody, like Sharons folks, if I ever get invited there.
11 – Live a cleen life knowing that faith in myself is the most important
12 – Keep *you* alive, Diary, & in you, the memory of Jack which many people already have begun to lose
13 – Not do rotten things to people unless they do it to me first.

Well, Diary, if I would of wrote in you last week rite after Chrismas I would of been on top of the world, but now I dont know. Woody come home the 24th & if you think Lary has changed for the worst, you ought to see Woody. He's wearing dark glasses too, but more than that, he managed to grow a beard after all & give away all his clothes except some blue cotton work shirts & work pants, and a great big wool blanket he throws over hisself thats made in Africa someplace out of wool wove so tight he says it sheds rain. Besides, he let his hair grow natural, (not that big gas-head conk he used to wear after a process) & its out so far now he looks like a black frizzy peecock.

I just had to laff when I saw him, but he said for me to shut my mouth, he wasent going wear white mans clothes any more, they made a false slave out of him, so the work clothes in memory of real slavery, but we had a black heratage going back to africa & the beard & natral hair & blanket was in memry of that. Then he really chewed his own blood brother Russel out. Russel showed up really strung out from that shit he's been pumping, with his arm full of needlemarkes & a 'white mans suit' on (just a plain wool suit like Woody used to wear all the time hisself) & Woody said Russel just what Whitey wanted him to be, a hophead failure who dident know any better than to dress like his master & go on dope from greeving over his own slavery. Big Ron still wears normal clothes, but Woody talked him & Leóna into changing, except Leona cant wear her African clothes to school to teach in or she'd get fired, so she just wears them at home, a long floppy dress, & a shirt they call a buba.

Well, thats the first thing, and *just* after I bought all these nice clothes – my blue coat, my white jersey dress, new black heels, and all that good lingeray – to look good for Woody when he got here. He said, who are you? What kind of *imatation* white whore are *you*? (But he got better later. It turned out when I got my new clothes off, I still had plenty that Woody wanted.)

Well, Woody went off Chrismas eve with Big Ron to a meeting & left Leona & Beverly & me with Mama Pope so we all went to serve at Rev Smiths, but there wasnt anybody but wemen & old men & little childern there. Woodys right. The Actions with the muslems & the Afro-Unity people now. Woody never come back all night, but he showed up about noon Chrismas & we had a good dinner & presents.

I give Woody a real good pen & pencil set (gentle hint to write me once in a while!) that was 24 carrot gold & cost $12.95. He said he liked it. I give Mama Pope a heeting pad that cost $6.50. Like I said, Woody give me the gold medalion. Chrismas night I went with Woody to the Hole-a-go-go. We heard somebody really on his way, Otis Redding, a good, raspy soul sound kind of like Sam Cooke. Later upstairs Woody told me to get my clothes off & then we talked old times. We had a big bag of grass to last us all vacation & split 3 or 4 joints naked in bed. Woody told me about Malcom X & Philly & the plans they got for next summer & I told him about college & Alice & Sharon & things you already know.

Woody said Alice was the worst, but Sharon the most dangerous. He called her a white liberel. He said they are the most dangerous on account of they want to help, so theyre always fooling people by making people think whites really care about the Problem. But all the time the Problems just as bad as ever, which is the blacks havent got money, or power, & never will have if they take the word of white liberels like Sharon that things is changing for the better. Things *not* changing, Woody said. The Whites got to get their back broke before they can know what Equal means.

Woody told me to call him Ali Ki Bar, but I woudent. That made him mad, but not really. He said if we went out, he wanted me to wear my old levis & denims from last summer, instead of my new jersey white dress, and I told him I woudent. So we stayed in the room, mostly.

Cheif Parkers boys come around like they always do stirring up trouble downstairs, but Woody got a drop down a drain pipe for the grass, which we keep in a plastic bag, in case they come up to the room. You can always swallow whats left of a joint, or send it to Long Beach if you can get to the can, & if they find the rest of the grass down the drain pipe, no way they can prove where it come from, unless they plant some in the room. Woody never in his whole life been busted for pot. He got busted twice back east for assault, but the SNCC lawyers plan to get him off on those charges. Woody works between SNCC & Malcom X, which is 2 difrent things, but for the same cause, so they need persons like Woody to keep them in touch with each other. To hear him & Big Ron talk, they plan to upset the whole country, but I cant hardly see them doing that. Big Ron cant even get Parker to put black cops in Watts, & if they cant do that, they arent hardly about to upset the whole country, they havent the money nor the power.

It rained something awful here, & big floods up north, hope Sharon dident get in them. She has a new car from her daddy for Chrismas by now, wonder what color?

Well, Woody & me just holed up in the room for 3 days. We went up to the Paladium in Hollywood (in my *white dress*, real short skirt, not my old levis) to hear Bobby Blue Bland & a good show, & got in some turmoil up there, but that was the only excitement. Bobby come out on stage & told us there wasent enough bread to sing for & walked out, but we'd all payed $5 each & there must of been 3000 persons there – I dont know how much bread Bobby wanted – so the persons started throwing chairs & busting tables. Woody dident want to get caught in that, so we split before the cops came. There went

$10, but there's nothing dummer than getting busted for something silly.

Woody & me was still on good terms even then, it wasent till that man named Franklyn met up with Woody at the Hole-a-go-go & we all went over to Mama Popes, that it happened. I gess Woody had told his friend Franklyn about Mama Popes power & Franklyn wanted to ask her about the future of the Problem, & the Black cause. Espesally about Malcom X, on account of Franklyn used to be a big-shot Black Muslim & wanted Mama Popes word on the future there, too. But she refused to tell Franklyn about Malcom X, or even Malik A Shabazz his new name.

Franklyn said to Woody, 'I come all the way down from Frisco for this & she wont even tell me.' 'Sometimes she cant,' Woody said. Then Franklyn said what reely was on his mind, 'Whats all this anyhow, you traipsing around here with some little rib dressed up like Lady Bird with dam near white skin & you supposed to be Afro, Woody? *Now,* old Mama Pope here wont tell me about Malik A. Shabazz. Some Afro *you* turning out to be.'

So Woody told Mama Pope to say about Malcom X, but she still woudent.

Then Franklyn said he was splitting & Woody could either come with him or not. Franklyn is a *bad* man. He's after power, all right, but mostly his own. I seen Woody get scared in his eyes. He said, again, for Mama Pope to tell about Malcom X & when she woudent, Woody told her to go to hell, her & her phoney cristal ball but when he said that, the lights dimmed all over like litening struck & she said if they knowed what was good for them, theyd all stay shy of Malcom X, his days was numbered.

Franklyn said, 'How many he got left?'

Mama Pope said, 'More than Abraham & less than George' (whatever *that* meant) & when Franklyn said to say it playn she shut up & woudent say another word. She panted hard, so I knowed she'd worked at it & wasent fooling. It smelled stuffy in there like stale greens. Franklyn said to Woody, 'She trying to put a hex on Malcom X?'

'Are you, Mama?' Woody wanted to know. But not another word from her. Then Franklyn said again was Woody staying here with 'this old badmouth witch & his little white-minded slut'? or coming with him? Woody left. I never seen him again. He went back to N.Y. with Franklyn about 3 days after that. I miss him awful.

January 10, Sunday

I sure miss Woody & wish he hadent of left in a huff. Diary, if i dont mention Alice again I hope you will understand. She is back, all right, but so disgusting I dont want to put her in my diary. She wont keep her hands off of me. All Lary does is get her hopped up from diddaling but of coarse he never comes & dosent care about her, only him, so chases her out of the practise room when *he* gives up in dispair. So Alice rushes back to the dorm looking for *me* to put out the fire. I told her what I thought of studs & dykes & she said she just coudent help it. Diary, I woudent mind so much if she just wanted it, & then over & done with, but she claims she's in *love* with me. Says I got the pretyest skin she ever touched & wants to hug & kiss me. I dont know what to do. I cant tell Prof Boileau or it woud disgust him too much. Mrs. Jameson the house mother would get us both kicked out, & now Woody run off & left me lonesome without a word. I got to stay in school. Mabey I'll tell Sharon except it woud disgust her too.

A lot been happening back east since Woody left, riots & marches. Him & Franklyn claimed 1 9 6 5 was going be a big year in the war, they wasent going to wait for spring to get started on the rebelion, & I beleeve it. But nothing happened to Malcom X yet like Mama Pope said.

I forgot to tell you, Bobby Kennedy had his 9th baby. (Ethyl did, I mean). God rest their poor dead Uncle may his soul soar high & proteck us all. Dr. King really stirring things up. He's trying to get the colored all over the south to sign up to vote, & the sheriffs giving him a rough time, but they scared to push him around too much, now he won the Peace Prize, lord bless him!

January 17, Sunday

Final tests next week. Prof. Boileau said I done so good in ANTHRO 476 he's going give me a C insted of a A. That is, it is *my* C, not *his* A, which he said was a pat on my back. (Diary, I am not perfect, & all, & I will be honest. I woud rather have *his* A than *my* C, now that it comes down to report cards, but embarassed to tell him. I know he is right, but hate to get my first C even if it is mine. Mabey I can tell Sharon to say that to him). MUSIC—432 I think I will get a C too, unless Lary desides to be nicer to me than he has been. MUSIC— 399???? Its supposed to be Indapendant Study for Lary, but havent done nothing for him since he got hot for Alice. Helth 120, B. P.E. 169 A as usual. These are my perdictions, we will see how I come out.

They finely arrested 18 more people for killing them 3 cival rights workers in Miss. last summer. They let them go last time & mabey they wont this, but who knows about Southern Justice?

January 20, Wensday

This has gone too far. Alice makes me didal her evrey night & to sleep with her. I haf to leave. Mabey I can get another room. I dont care *how* much money or clothes she gives me. Besides, the clothes dont fit anyhow.

January 21, Thursday

Talked to Mrs. Jameson. She said not a chance to change, unless I had a good reason. Cant tell her the reason. Alice after me again last night. Went back to my own bed after I did it to her & she fell asleep & then started Farting.

January 22, Friday

Well, Diary, gess who is my frend again?

Lary.

He called me to practise after the final in MUSIC 432 & said he'd give me a A if I coud help him out. (Diary, I dident do it altogether for the A, but also for Lary's sake who needed help). So we had our first practise in a long long time & – wonder of wonders – he moaned & groaned with a genuine hard on till I thoght sure he was going to pop off hollering 'good news' *Yo Hear* about the people in Hungary rising up this week. 'Oh! Oh! *This* is the time we're going to *beat Rusia*!!!'

But when the miracle dident happen Lary turned very mean in a way I never saw before & wanted to hurt me, he feels polatics that strong. I got a real bruise on my leg to prove it where he whupped me, is this something Alice has been getting him to do? I dont know, but I think he's turning bad & probly plans on hurting me again if he cant come. Mabey I better not go back, A's or not, even though he said it was sure good to get back beside me & my skinny little tan ass after . . . (he never said her name, he probly thinks I dont know) . . . after being off of me so long.

So, I get my A in both MUSIC 432 & 399 & liked it beter than I ever did with Lary before, till he hit me, not to speak of what a relief to be away from Alice fat-finger.

January 24, Sunday

Poor Nat King Cole. I gess he got lung cancer bad. Jack & my Diary, pray for the safety of Nat Cole, he's been a good man all his life. My stepdaddy knowed Nat King Cole & said he's a man with a big hart. Hope he gets well. Churchill dyed over in London, but it was *time* for him. Besides, who cares about him? Poor Rev King got slugged down in Selma, Ala, by 2 or 3 white men in a hotel lobby. All Rev King did was get the colored there to sign up to vote. They arrested 200 negroes already this week & sent troopers in to keep them in jail. More power to Rev King! Alice says her daddy says Rev King ought to be cast – rated like they used to down home, & I coud of hit her. Somethings got to give. Its too much sleeping in the same room with Alice, let alone in her awful creaky bed when she makes me. I wish she dident give me so much money.

January 31, Sunday

Dear Diary. I am going to leave. I told Prof. Boileau – not about Alice, but that I had to leave for a while & he's very upset. He said I *had* to stay this Spring Term on account of I would be literate by next June & needed steady tests till then. Thats why I signed up for what I did this Spring, all Anthro:

ANTHRO	476	Field Study	(4)	
ANTHRO	325	Ethnological Music	(3)	
ANTHRO	326	Fokelore	(3)	
ANTHRO	362	Esetics of Non-litarate Peop.	(3)	
P. E.	169	Dance & Rythm	(1)	(last time, thank the Lord)
			14	

You see I am taking 14 credits instead of 12, which is almost a full load. Prof Boileau said if I quit, his whole 2 yrs. work will be 'scrubbed'. You see, too, I am out from under Lary. Whatever happens from now on with Lary will be for friends, not for grades.

Speaking of grades, my perdictions come true except for 1. Prof Boileau had a weakening of the hart & *did* give me a A in ANTHRO 476. Sharon said I really deserve it on account of he going to print a whole lot of articals about me & get a raise in pay for it so I was worth A. That means I got all A's again except Health, which is B. Lary was true to his last minute word. Alice only got B in her MUSIC & she was so dam mad at Lary she said she wanted to scratch his balls off. I was scared to tell her what I got. I said C when she made me, so that made her feel like her B was worth more than it was. But that isent why I want to leave, of coarse, its the *other* thing which is worse than ever. Alice keeps giving me things, but her rings & bracelets too big & they fall off, & none of her clothes fit, & she keeps wanting to take me to the show & even give me money. I take the money.

We seen Cleopatra with Elizabeth Tailor last week & she wanted to put her hand in my pants during the movy. She's really a mess! I told Sharon I'd drop out if I dident get another room mate. She dident ask why but maybe gessed. Sharons MG this year is green with green lether. Mama Pope hasent heard from Woody since he left in a huff but Ron says he's okay & maybe even going to France with Malcom X. Ron heard it from Malcom X hisself. Malcom X snuck in & out of here last week, but Woody wasent with him. Well, I hope he has a good time in France, maybe he can find somebody besides a 'white minded slut' to fuck.

They killed some poor black boy in Miss. this week – some Sheriff killed him, & they let the Sheriff go.

Poor Ollie Shelby, another poor 18 year old who got killed, they had 600 at his funeral, but 125,000 turned out to see Churchills grave.

Lary put in a call for me yesterday but I was so wore out with Alice, & so scared of Lary, I snuck off to the Student Union &

watched TV instead. Those bruses he give me last week are still sore.

1 little note of joy. Alice got a Kennedy ½ dollar in change at the movy & let me keep it. They have been out for quite a while, but dumb persons keep hording them. My *1st*, & will carry it for luck but not spend it. It is dated 1 9 6 4.

Febuary 4, Thursday

Lary put in a desprate call for me. Like a dum bunny I went. Wont ever go again, since he is really getting mean. He wanted to spank me. I let him a little, but when it got to smarting bad I told him to stop but he woudent. He wanted to whip me, but I got dressed & ran for it. Had on my very old blue shift, which is still his favrite. He tryed to keep me in & we knocked some things over. The picture he got on the piano of George (I forget his name) fell off & broke. Lary said he woud get me for that but I dont know how he can get me any worse than he has, with his pinching & hitting. I wish he'd go back to Alice, that woud take the load off both ends. I am sick & depressed. Started flowing this morning. 5 days late & scared, (but why be scared? Cant get knocked up by *neether* Lary nor Alice.) Where is Woody tonite? I think flying the Osean, I feel him flying the Osean. I am brused & sore from Lary. The world is too much & I want to cry but dont know who to cry on. Evreybody dead or gone I never felt so blue since poor Jack . . . Poor Rev King got throwed in Jail for marching in Selma, Alabama. They arrested *3000* by now & still havent relented on colored people signing up for voting except a few at a time – 35 out of 900 in 2 whole years, but for the whites, 950 out of 1200. Thats how they keep folks down, with the vote. How do they keep *me* down? By telling me I'm lucky to be here with Lary, & me scared to say difrent because I havent any *real* place to go home to, like Sharon does. If I'm so bad, how come evrybody always want to fuck & diddle me? Thats difrent, isent it? Do they think I want their white cock & finger? Well, I do, if thats the only way I can get their money, too, thats how they make me feel. Someday I'll have *all* them things like Sharon got & Alice, & then we'll see who phones who up for a fuck when things get blue. Blue Blue

Black & Blue
You fuck me
& i'll fuck you
Oh, hell. . . . I need to get high.

Febuary 12, Friday

Told Sharon this week I coudent study any more I'm so depressed & disgusted with the World. I think I'm right about Woody. He's in England now with Malcom X, but they woudent let them in Paris. Malcom X said Paris just like South Africa, they wont let any blacks in but Uncle Toms. Rev King seen LBJ the other day, but what can *they* do about it when you got the hate you got in the world?

Those poor blacks in Selma, the Sheriff busted 160 of them & made them go on a 6 mile hike in the wet & cold, just to humble them.

Ringo Starr got maryed. His woman is only 18, which brings up somthing only I in the whole world knows tonite, Diary, it is my 17th birthday. Sharon nearly 21. Alice & me tryed sneaking in a topless bar last Wed. They are the kind where the waitresses go with absalutely bare tits when they give you beer. They are all over the place now. But we got kicked out, of coarse. Alice all hot to see some wemens tits, as if she dosent get enough in the dorm shower rooms. Seen a funny thing on the news tonite, a guy named Perry *Loving* coudent mary his wife in Virginia on acount of she's part indian & part black. *Loving*. I call it funny, but honest, Diary, I am getting sick of the U.S. of A. & college & evreybody in it, except 1 or 2. I got to go see Mama Pope to find out what to do.

Feburary 15, Monday

I am very woryed. They throwed a firebom at Malcom X's house in N.Y. but luckaly his poor wife & 4 dauters dident get hurt. Somebody out to get him. I wonder if Woody back from England yet. I read in Ebony where Cassius Clay says 'Mr. Eliza Muhammad will destroy Malcom X thru Allah. You dont buck Mr. Muhammad & get away with it.' Sounds like theyre working some roots on him like the west Indians do.

Mama Pope said to *absalutely* stay in college, her kristal ball said. I would like to learn how to read it sometime.

Nat Cole dyed tonite – it just happened over the radio. The poor man dident have a chance. I am *never* going to smoke (except grass) *or* drink exsept when I have to, not to be a square ect. I pray for Nat's safe journey to heaven & ask Jacks soul to help Nat assend to the lap of our god who looks over all his childern, Amen.

Feburary 19, Friday

They buryed Nat today between Gracy Allen & Alan Ladd who was old-time stars. I cant study at all theres so much going on. I told Sharon in the lab this week either I move out from Alice or back to Watts. I can get a job in Watts any time now I had this much college (& all A's) – maybe I coud even get a skolarship someplace else, but Sharon said I woud have to pass *real* tests & coudent yet. Maybe she's right. They tryed to blow up the Statue of Liberty on Tusday. Some kid graduated from Belmont high was in on it. Diary, you can imagine how much Lary needed me when *that* hapened. He called.

But I woudent go.

I am thru with Lary & his black glasses & shirt & pants & limp cock & picture of George Lincoln Rockwell who Sharon says is a Natzi. He looks it, on Larys piano. Well, some Calif.

college kids finely felt what it was like to be nigger. That Selma Sheriff James Clark slugged them like poor Rev King got slugged the other day. The Troopers had their fun, too, they clubbed 400 poor black people coming out of church, beat up 10 & shot 1. Whites are calling it 'savage'. Same in N.Y. 300 ran loose beating & stealing, & I say, why not? Death is in the air. I can smell it, like rancid life, cold & stale like a room where Mama Pope is dead in, I'm afraid, Diary. This war we're in going to reach out like a devil whirlpool & suck us all under.

Febuary 26, Friday

Dear Diary. I feel like I been to hell & then felt the hand of God lift me from the dead.

I will try to tell you all that happened in this last week that seems like a year. The pen that writes this down in you, in the memory of J.F.K., is in a hallowed hand which, *less than a day ago*, shook the soft hand of Rev Martin Luther King himself.

Yes, its true.

That saintly man touched me & smiled at me & I feel like I been blessed from angles in the pit of hell, lifted bodily from the damned.

1. I am home from school today, but am *living at Sharons* now. That is the first thing. Never again will I need to let Alice roll on me & hug me & rap her awful legs around mine. Free.

2. Woody is safe, too, in spite of the fack that poor fated Malcom X is *ded*, mowed down by assasins bullets like poor Jack, while his wife betty said the same words as poor Jacky in her moment of Trajedy, 'They're killing him!' He had just rose to speak. 'Brothers & Sisters,' he said when the shots rung out. The police in N.Y. claim the Black Muslems done it but who knows – and who cares now, after being touched by Rev King?

3. He healed my awful week. When I heard on TV about Malcom X I was sure poor Woody had dyed too. I passed out. I never passed out before, that I remember. It was in the dorm

lounge. They took me unconsous to the infirmary & give me a shot. When I come to, they let me call Big Ron who found out already Woody was okay. Woody was there when it happened but the bullets missed him.

4. Then they said I coud leave the infirmary which is when I had my second relapse, & realized how I coud never go back to the same room as Alice. I went into histerics that I can only partly remember, & when I come to from the *second* shot, Prof. Boileau was at my side with Sharon. They conforted me & I cryed & cryed. I am beginning to love them. The whole year they been kind & not knowed my lonelyness & anguish partly because they're so secure & partly because I, Trixie Mae, woud not tell them my anguish. I was too proud & young.

But I told them in the infirmary (between my sobs) & how I was ready to dye, but not go back to Alice. Prof. Boileau was plain mad at Alice & himself, but Sharon understood & calmed him down. Prof. Boileau said it was all his falt, he had put his projeck ahead of me, his work before a human life. Sharon said the projeck counted too, & woud I come to her pad for a few days while I got better? She said me watching the awful things evrey nite on TV, & having to sleep with dirty sick Alice, had broke my poor hart & spirit.

I cryed again (I cryed a hole years worth that 1 night).

So that explayns it. Harlem still seething with hate & misry after Malcom X's death. Theyre going to shut down all the stores in Harlem for a week in memory of his death. Rev. King's life threatened & a man arrested for having a ton of dynamite to do the job, & Eliza Muhammad says Malcom X got what he preached & whoever trys to get *him* will get the same, but . . .

The whole world may seethe in hate, but I have been thru my hate & out into the light. Rev. King come to L.A. to the Paladium in Hollywood where me & Woody went last Chrismas to see Bobby Blue Bland when they tore the joint apart. But this time so difrent! Sharon got her & me tickets. Rev. King was raising money for the black cause. (I give $10) He talked. He's got the nicest, darkest richest voice. Then afterwards Sharon & me hung around & shook his hand. He said to me, 'I'm pleased to meet you,' like he meant it, looked right in my eyes. He's a nice big man. I coudent even talk, but it was a healing touch & last nite I slept so long I dident even hear Sharon leave for class today. I think I'm all well now. Sharon & Prof. Boileau brung all my things from the dorm (I had to tell her where the money was). (Alice said part of it was hers when Sharon took it from underneath the desk top, but Sharon just said, 'I'll let you settle that with Trixie when she gets well,' & brung it all to me.) I dont think Sharon even looked in the envelope to see how much was there $135) (which woud be nothing, for Sharon).

Febuary 27, Saturday

Sharon says to look on the *posative* side of things. Thats easier to do when you got money, but I dident tell her that. Malcom X buryed today, his funeral on TV but I dident see Woody. Sharon says not to watch TV so much, its bad for you.

March 3, Wensday

Sharon all upset today. They arrested somebody named Maryo Savio up at Berkeley. Its difrent when its somebody *you* know gets arrested. Sharon says we are going to demonstrate down here like they did at Berkeley. But I havent seen any action yet. Demonstrate for what?

March 4, Thursday

Big funeral in Alabama for another poor negro killed a few days ago, wonderful Rev King in the lead. The poor negro was slugged trying to register, then shot in the stomache by 1 of Gov

Wallaces Troopers. I think that poor black man is the one we ought to greeve, not Maryo Savio. Sharon says we ought to greeve them both, America is tottering.

March 7, Sunday

Doing better at school, & back on the tests in the Lab. Diary, I never told you about Sharons *really cool* pad. Its only 6 blocks from campus up on the secont story with my fold-out blue sofa & Sharons big bedroom with the white & gold headbord beds. She got *tons* of records – Peter Paul & Mary, Beatles, The Supremes (Where Does Love Go?), – & a *cool* hi fi with 2 speakers. She bys all the food but I pay ½ the rent from my lab mony but still leaves loads left over. I sleep in the living room which is better on account of Sharon reads a lot late at nite & I can watch TV. The toilet & bathtub & wash basin are *avacado* color & so is the sink & icebox. You can go barefoot anywhere wall to wall on the fuzzy yellow carpet. A lamp hangs over my sofa that moves up & down. I coud live here forever. Even the rug smells clean & excepting after a shit the bathroom smells like the rest of the house, too. Sharon has some cool friends who dont mind smoking a joint at nite, but in this bilding we got to be careful & usally in the bathroom & let the fan take the smell out. Her friends is beatniks mostly. They wear sandels & have beards, but talk sweet like Sharon. I dont think there is a bad mouth amongst them all. Sharons girl friends named Stefanny & Betty & Dee, whose as tall as a boy & will be a model someday. Their boy frends named Ed the one who stutters & Gene & Andy & I forget 2 or 3 others. Andy took a liking to me & likes to hang around.

Sometimes when I get tired I go to be in Sharons other bed & they stay in the living room to talk & hear sound. Sometimes they stay all night but usally dont. Thay are all *very* much for Rev King & say not very nice things about LBJ & the war in Viet-Nam & are very much for Maryo Savio. Thay all like me, I think, except Betty & Dee who I think is jelous I live with

Sharon, but they keep there mouths shut about it. Nothing really big, but I can feel it.

Sometimes I cook for Sharon. She likes what I fix. Last night we had pork chops & yams. Sharon never ate collard greens in her life. You cant even by them out here. Sweet potato pie. Sharons friends all make fun of persons like Lary, who they call a lovely, plastic Natzi & ought to be fired. They was laffing last night at a man who is head of the Jon Burch Club. He said Rev King was a hippocrit who the Commys trained to start a black Russia down south, all part of a plot started back in 1930 or so with Roossafelt.

I wish that man coud meet Rev King *just once*, he woud never say that again. Yesterday Rev King talked to the Presadent again. Mabey it was about that Sheriff who used cattle prods full of electricity against the marches in Selma.

March 9, Tuesday

School okay but Sharon says if I dont quit watching TV shes going to bust it for my good. Last night I seen Gov Wallaces Troopers beat up some poor marchers while they neeled to pray on a bridge. They hurt 67 on the Governers orders, it said. It made me sick. Sharons Uncle told people in Congress how awful Gov. Wallace was, but that dosent heel the wounds of them poor 67. Where is Woody? On the news tonight it said Clark Kerr who is head at Berkaly quit. Sharon got all upset over that. I told her mabey *she* better not watch TV, neither.

March 15, Monday

Yesterday we marched from Pershing Square to the Fedral Bilding singing We Shall Over Come, about 20 blocks. 6000, the paper said. They are good people I dont see why Woody says they arent & are hurting the Cause. Sneeky White Liberals, he calls them. They are *helping* the Cause. 5 of us drove downtown jammed in Sharons green MG with the top down. *Cool*, man, & when them cats down on Figuroa seen me in that car, dident thay give *me* the eye. Sharon lets me wear nearly anything of hers, & they all fit. (Shes not fat like you-know-who, whose name I wont menshun) I had on a bright green nit cap that tyes under your chin, & a sweater to match. My tits bigger than Sharons so I *really* fill it out, almost too much. Later we went to a service for poor Rev. Reeb who got beat to death in Selma. 600 of us, the news said.

After these marches we can hardly wait to hear what the news says. Andy (I like Andy, but he's high too much) says he dosent beleeve the march really happens till he sees it on TV, even tho he was there. That isent true, of coarse, but its a litel like that. Andy found a kitten on the march. He left it here. Its name is Selma, for the march. it likes me best, I think. It is gray. It is so wobbly it cant hardly walk. It sleeps with me.

March 19, Friday

Sharon went out tonight. Andy come over alone. He wants to fuck me but I dont think I better for Sharons sake. She migt get mad. He says funny things, like the king of egipt dyed today in a restraunt he weighed 285 lbs, Andy said they named a college after him & called it Farouk U. When Andy gets started he makes up funny things in a string. Andy isent pushy, but he told me how much he wanted to 'Farouk' me. He is majoring in Anthro too but not at our college. He's trying to grow a beard but dosent amount to much except under his nose, I think he will have to settel for a mustache. We played with Selma for a long time. Andys happy doing nothing. His daddy has money. We poped some popcorn & put some on a string. Selma chased it. I let Andy kiss me but thats all. We split a joint (his grass) but I made him smoke it in the bathroom. Its really a dum law where they can bust you for 5 to 15 years for just having a joint *on* you. Andy thinks so to. They throwed 36 preachers in jail in

Selma today at the courthouse for leading 3000 in honor of poor Rev Reeb.

March 27, Saturday

Dear Diary. Sharon keeps telling me to just mind my own bisness, study my lessons, do my lab work, & keep my mind & soul off of the L.A. Times & TV, but she dosent understand. Woody may of gone off & left me, but that dosent mean I can just turn him off, like that, any more than Sharon can turn off her Uncle, just like that. She's always looking for his name in the paper about Washingtown, D.C., just like I keep looking for news from Woody & Big Ron ect ect who's fighting back east in the war while I'm doing questions for Sharon & Prof Boileau. Thay killed this poor woman Mrs. Liuzzo yesterday in Selma, & Gov Wallace wont even give the time of day to them *30,000*! brave persons who been marching thru the South.

But, it isent all bad. They named a mountain peek for Jack up in Canada. Yesterday Bobby climed it. It is very high, & Bobby fell down a ice hole on the way up but dident get hurt. I finely let Andy fuck me last nite but wasent very good. I dont think I will let him again. We get along just as good when we dont, & he fucks weak like he has to ask his mothers permission first.

April 4, Sunday

Late. Am laying on the sofa. The bed is made up. The window open. I can smell the night air fresh. The smell of traffic fades. Sharon in her room reading. She thinks I'm taking study notes. Selma kitty purring between my tits. I got my candy stripe pj's on, it will get cold tonite. Somebody just went to the can next door, I can hear the water flush thru the wall.

Today I took Sharon to see Mama Pope. Her sink stopped up

last week so Russel undid the pipe & run it out to the yard. Now the yard smells like old soap & stale greens. Mama says when Ron gets back he can fix it, but Sharon *already this morning* phoned a plummer down. Just like that! Mama says Woodys been in Alabama all this time with something called Black Panthers that never get in the paper or on TV, they are secret. Maybe he'll be out here this summer to start the Black Panthers here, Mama said. Him & Big Ron both in Lousiana now, & things'll start poping there any day. Sharon asked her who woud be presadent next time & Mama Pope said, 'Away, away with LBJ, another nose will rule the day' which dident help much. I made Mama Pope camomile tea & we talked. We sat on the front porch by the plaster lion where you cant smell the back yard so bad. Sharon likes the lion, & asked Mama if she brung it from texas? 'All I brung from texas was a used railroad ticket & a change of shoes,' Mama said. She told Sharon how she worked around L.A. (mostly beverly hills) till she got too old. Now she lives on food stamps & welfare, & what she makes off fortunes. Sharon has a nice way that Mama likes, of setting very quiet, on the lion, say, asking questions full of simpathy so its Mama who ends up feeling good, & not just Sharon prying. Mama told Sharon about her daddy stealing the horse for texas & then sending it back after a hundred miles, so as not to steal it. Sharon said she wished *her* grandaddy been that honest, but Mama said not to falt her grandaddy, the dead got there own worrys. Mama blew haf a joint but dident offer Sharon. She probly thinks Sharon dosent know pot. Some of Sharons friends from back east & around are in Selma & Mama asked her if it was true like the man in Congress said this week on TV the marchers all drunk & sex orgys & they got people to march for $10 a day & all the body you coud get. But Sharon said no, theyre lyes.

Mama Pope kissed Sharon on the cheek when we left. She sayd she'd croshay a blanket for Sharon if she brung her favorite color yarn, so Sharon plans yellow, the same eyes and mystic marks as Mama's purple one. She's excited about it.

Sharons brother Dicky, who is 15, might be down over easter.

April 6, Tuesday

Diary, I have to tell you a funny thing happened in Washingtown D.C. yesterday. The *mayor* of Selma got Murpheyd out of $167 by some black man. I gess the mayor was looking for you-know-what & this black man said he could get it for him, & then took off with the money. Well, $167 isent a whole lot, but its something to put on the bill.

I'm sorry, Diary, not to write much, but I am real busy in school & going out with Sharon's gang – the s.d.s. they call themselves, I dont know what that means, but since I am not lonesome, dont write in you so much, but promise to try to keep up the news for you (& Jack) at *least* Once a week. I still love you very much.

April 9, Friday

Out to a movy in 10 minutes with the s.d.s Just to tell you all okay. Sharons brother *defanately* for easter. More later. p.s. 's.d.s.' stands for Students for a demacratic sosiety. They blow a lot of pot & plan on helping the blacks in their struggel.

April 18, Easter Sunday

Well, Diary, I promised last time to write in you every week, & the first thing I done let nearly 2 weeks go by.

Sharon took Dicky her brother to the airport just now so I am home quiet & *alone* for the first time in many days, so hope you understand. Dicky come down from Montaray for Easter Vacation & to celebrate Sharons 21st birthday on the 15th. A very quiet boy but *oh so nice*, hardly a beard yet but what he has he lets grow in golden down (like Woodys scrawny). He is already taller then Woody & still growing, but skinny except nice wide sholders which he will grow into. He dosent look much like Sharon except both fair. Sharons eyes is blue but Dickeys brown. Sharons nose is petite, but Dickys nose firm & bold. He looks a littel like a hawk except his eyes big & mild & soft. That comes from being rich. That is, both Sharon & Dicky seem to have got past that sertain hurty age without having got *mean & hurt* like Woody & Ron (& me), because theyre so rich they can see love in evreything. It makes nice folks out of them in spite of what Woody thinks about rich folks. Dicky is a Junior in high school & gets his own car next year on his 16 birthday. They have another brother whose a lot younger. Dicky plays a gitar pretty good already, and when I asked him what he wanted to be, a gitar player? he said, why not? You can say things like that when your rich.

Sharons birthday the best birthday party I ever went to. We had most of it down at Andys place in Venice. *What* a place! He lives in the canals where instead of streets you got water in the front yard (& you park in alleys in back). Little jumpy bridges just wide enuff for 1 car join the blocks. Its all run down, side-walks along the canals caved in, slanty & slippery from the scummy water. Andy lives in a dark red house where you climb some stares under a big grapevine, they going to tear these houses all down soon & bild a fancy boat club, Andy says, but meantime, cheap rent. He likes to paint pictures & his pad is painted in the craziest colors, mostly orange & yellow in one room, all zigzaggy, & another one completely in black. No chairs, you just sit on the floor. All the table legs cut off. Andy got a terrific hi fi. You cant tell where the sound comes from, the speakers is all over, & hid. He has some groovy albums, Woody & me had good sounds over the hole-a-go-go, but Andy's set up for really outer-space. All the pot & sound you want & Andys an acid head, it turns out, so any time I want a trip its okay – but *I will never* take LSD. I seen what happened to poor Russel on cocaine (they finely busted him last week & he's off in some rehab farm now, Leona says).

Anyhow, the nice thing about Andy's pad is, these white people is rich, & white, & you arent afraid of getting busted about every 5 minutes. I dont mean they dont get busted, they do, but not so often as down at Watts before the Man started getting scared, & here, you always got somebody to spring you, like your folks lawyer, & can always get more money. I mean, this makes all the difrence, instead of like poor Russel, spent most his time on the street pushing, just to get enough stuff to keep body & soul together, all strung out on the stuff. Sharons friends dont have to worry like that. They mostly all got cars, & there dads can get insurance & stuff & the tires is good, not like Big Ron used to be before he started living with Leona. Used to be, if you made it clean uptown in Rons hog without a flat it was a big deal, or having the Man stop you on a phoney bust.

Well, Diary, I wont go into all the groovy details, but we had a *groovy* dinner brung in from a chinee place (my fortune cookie: YOU WILL MEET A STRANGE YOUNG MAN) & set around hearing music & getting clued-in on grass. Even Dicky had some. It turns out his birthday is exackly the same day as mine (Lincolns Birthday) & he's exackly 2 yrs younger. That makes him 15, but he is big for his age & has a lot of cool. You do, if your rich.

Dicky slept on the sofa (with Selma) & I slept in the other bed in Sharons room. Sharon snores. It dosent bother you in the other room, but is sure loud beside her. But Im not complaining, dont get me wrong. They are 2 of the finest persons in the world (not to speak of way out & groovy). We talked a lot. They like their uncle, of coarse, but Dicky thinks he is rather crule – but dosent hold that too much against him since they say you got to be crule to stay in power like a Senator. I asked them if they thought Jack F. K. was crule & they said even him, too. & *Bobby*, very defanately. For 1 thing, he is a Scorpio, & for another he isent very tall like Napoleon. They said he ran a very dirty campain in N.Y. for Senator, but it seems hard to beleeve he got kids & still crule & dirty like that, but I suppose so. Not Jack, tho, no matter what Dicky & Sharon say.

We talked about a lot of things, how the acter Ronny Regan might run for governor but not a chanst to win, how they're going to have a new car for LBJ even *more* bullet proof than Jacks old one, with another bubble. It will cost $325,000, if you can figure that out for just 1 car! LBJ hardly seems worth it, they said. They are so upper class they think he's a cracker.

I told them about Woody, now that the Lousiana trouble started in Bogalusa where the KKK Night Riders out swapping shots with the blacks, & no sheriff to help. Today the news said 600 out marching against the Klan, probly led by Woody & Ron. Meanwhile another poor lynching in a Adlanta jailhouse, & more smoke & gas bombs, but Sharon said, look on the bright side: we got Medacare thru the House for folks like Mama Pope.

'And they finely let a negro page into congress,' Dicky said, but the way he says things, your never sure but if he's smiling.

April 26, Monday

School okay. I am getting a little fatter, but not fat. I do all the cooking now & sharon loves it more all the time. Dident even watch TV tonight. Can still smell the pork chops baked in sour cream. Sharon says this place getting like Mamas, with all the spices lined up on the shelf & warm smells. Used clove & savory & bay leaves in the chops, and Mmmmmmm.

April 27, Tuesday

They arrested 3 KKK for killing Mrs Violet Liuzzo but predict the jury will let them go. Troopers beat up 20 praying blacks in Ala. A black boy got shot in another town. School okay.

April 28, Wensday

How can I hold to 1 sentence today? Rev King talked at UCLA today. Sharon & me & most the S.D.S. went. I *love* that man. He told us that 200 negroes got fired from there jobs in

Selma for just signing up to vote. & the rest of them got to vote *right* at the next election, *or* else *they'll* get fired. Rev King needs money for these people. I give $20. Sharon the same. Dicky woud to, if he was here. Nearly 5000 students at the turnout for that *lovely* man. I tryed to see him later to say hello again, but coudent even get close.

April 29, Thursday

Postcard from Dicky. He likes my cooking. He wants to come back this summer. Its a crazy world. That boy has *evreything*, & all he wants to do is get away from home.

April 30, Friday

Seen 'The VIPs' with Liz Tailor & Richard Berton, with Andy, Sharon & Betty. A good picture, I thought. Wanted to stay, but they thought it was so bad we all walked out ½ way through singing We Shall Over Come. I was embarassed. The manager threatened to call the Man, but dident when we left. To the beach later. One joint each. Good high, still on it, I gess. Andy wanted to stay here all night, *but not with Sharon here* I told him & woudent go back to his pad with him. Love you, Diary.

May 1, Saturday

Laudromat in the morning as usal. The U.S. Marines took over Santo Domingo yesterday. Some got killed. Everybody in S. America sore about it. Lary probly shagging Alice in the practise room on account of it right now. To think how long I had to put up with Lary! Stayed home tonight. Sharon out. Andy come. Stayed just long enough to do it. Think Im flowing, &

he's onely been gone ½ hr, guess he sprang me loose. Will just lay around tomorrow maybe stew a chicken.

May 2, Sunday

Stewed the chicken but wasent nearly enough. Ed & Gene dropped in with Stefanny & Betty. All of us split 2 joints. Wasent worth it. Ed & Stefanny stayed here while we went out & seen Jack Lemon in 'Underneath of the Yum Yum Tree', a dum movy. They did it on the sofa while we was out. I can still smell Ed's scum underneath of my sheet.

May 3, Monday

School normal. Looks like the U.S. of A. has taken over the Dominican Republic. Note from Lary today with Prof Boileau's secratary. Wants to try it, but I tore it up. Seen Alice. She told me to come up to the dorm if I needed money. Screw her.

May 5, Wensday

School okay. Had lunch in the caf with Andy. We come back from school early. He just cant get enough. He always has some grass on him. Somday he will get caught. Split 2 joints.

May 7, Friday

Well, Diary, they let the people go who killed Mrs Liuzzo just like I bet they woud. The jury coudent agree – not for murder, but only manslawter. That is, Diary, they coudent even agree on a *little* penalty, let alone a true one. Sharon just as upset as me, for once. I told her she ought to quit watching TV (ha ha).

May 9, Sunday

Seen Mama Pope. She said Woody due back any day, but she told me to *stay out of Watts*, the people there getting ugly & mean over all thats happened like letting them 3 people go on Mrs Liuzzo. Leona & Beverly say the same, but they think I ought to go back to Watts & live, like Big Ron says, instead of with Sharon, or else I lose touch. But they agreed the more school I get the better. Mabey I could be a teacher like them someday. I wonder. They make good money, & Leona & Ron got a big new hog with 4 good tires now. What shoud I do, Diary? Go back to Watts & lose all this?

May 10, Monday

Seen on TV tonight where them 2 Klan men let go on Mrs Liuzzo led a parade to celebrate the 4th anniversary of blowing up a Freedom Rider bus years ago. Made me sick – really. Took 2 asprin for headache & stomache & still feel bad.

May 12, Wensday

Dear Diary. Good news!

Sharon asked me today to stay with her at the pad this *summer*, too, not just till schools out. She's going to do Field Study under Prof Boileau for summer term & he said I coud do the same if I want. *No dead Indians* this time, tho. They want to set up field study down in Watts & want me to help. If I do, I can get 4 credits of A again for practicly nothing.

I started to wonder what will Big Ron & Woody think, that I am some kind of chickenshit white-on-white-on-white? But decided thats my bisness, not theres. Dont know for sure what to do. Help me think, Diary. (its sure better here than down at Mama Popes lumpy sofa & no air cooler all summer)

May 14, Friday

Diary, so much *happens* all the time. They're back to bombing churches in Miss. again. I have a feeling about this summer. I dont know about taking Prof Boileau & Sharon down in Watts & poking around on a field study. Its difrent with dead Indians. *They're* dead. On the other hand, if people like Prof Boileau dont care about the getto & the persons in it, who will? Jacky & little John-John & Carolyn in England to dedicate a statue of Jack. The darlingest & saddest picture in the paper of Carolyn wiping away a tear. Yes, Diary, tears are still being wiped away for that dear man. Mine, too. Tears of loyalty to my country, & sadness in its present need.

May 17, Monday

Woody better watch his step. I think him & his SNCC & Black Panthers gone too far, now they even got CORE & NAACP & the KKK *all* down on Them. You can only go so fast on this, & like CORE says, the negroes is *very* rude, & NAACP says they dont have any responsibility (Woody *does* get that look in his eye – I seen it many times) & the KKK says Woody & his kind trying to overthrow the U.S. of A, which nobody will stand for, not even Sharon. I feel something black in my hart which is a cloud of doom, not a core of joy.

May 18, Tuesday

Diary, I shoud tell you about my classes this term, but promise not to drag it out like I used to. I am doing *good* & am nearly on my own. Prof Boileau said he told my teachers to take it easy on me, & I guess they will on account of *he* is the head of their department, but even so, the only thing they take it easy on is my spelling, which I am still working on but having a hard time. I got to get the answers *on my own*, Prof Boileau says, & he has faith in me.

Diary, you already know what I am taking, but will tell you more. My ANTHRO 476 is field study which just means the last of the lab tests. I am nearly completely litarate now & am taking the same tests over I done nearly 2 yrs ago, to see the difrence. Will get A for that. My ANTHRO 325 is ethnological music which scared the pants off me till I found out all they meant by that was Jazz. Chico Hamilton, Rex Stewart, ect. Well, I know as much about that as the man who teaches it, who is not a regular teacher, but comes out here just to teach that 1 coarse. He dident go to college neither, but knows all these cats who play Jazz. I am a cinch A in that, Mr, Chatsworth, who teaches it, grades evreybody easy, I heard. Thats 1 way he keeps his classes big so they keep hiring him to teach it. My step daddy knew Rex Stewart too.

Then my ANTHRO 326 is Folklore taught by a woman Mrs. Hayes. Folklore has to do with stories like step daddy used to tell, & once in a while Mama Pope tells them, but not any more. They are basicly fairy tails told all over the world & a lot of them have to do with the black people & Indians, like animal storys where brer rabbit rode brer fox like horseback for a joke, & things like that. I probly wont get a A in there on account of this is *litrature* & my spelling is . . . well, I dont have to tell *you*, Diary.

Then I got ANTHRO 362 which is Esthetics of Non-Litarate People which is the hardest. Esthetics scared my pants off too till I found out it meant that people who *cant* read & write, do difrent kinds of paintings & statues ect as people who *can*. Luckyly Prof Boileau teaches this so . . . if he is kind to me this time I will get a A in this. Then there is P.E. 169 Dance & Rhythm which I am so sick of Miss Lench, & she so sick of me, after 2 yrs of the same old exercises (to the same old records) she will give me a A just to celebrate this being my last time.

So, I have rambeled way too long, Diary, but had to, to tell you what I am learning this time. School gets out June 12, less than 1 *mo*.! Time has sure flied since coming to Sharons. I feel lucky & glad to be alive at this time.

May 19, Wensday

Diary, I got 2 big long term papers done & am behind in my reading for Mrs. Hayes. Just going to have to let you go for a while unless somthing crusial comes up.

June 13, Sunday

Dear Diary. I coudent believe my eyes when I looked. Nearly a month! I knowed it was a long time – the longest ever – away from you, but a *month*! That just goes to show it isent real time that counts, but just how long it *seems*. Well, as you can imagine, I been busy busy busy. First the term papers & then the final exams. Diary, I think I am maybe smarter than I thought before. As you know, I think I am okay & not shy about it, except certain dum things I do like still caring about people like Woody, but do you know what? I got all A's again. This is getting to be funny. I know I had lots of help from Prof Boileau but even *he* was surprised this time, since I am mostly on my own.

Well, the summer is set. Sharons keeping the pad, & doing the field work in Watts with me & Prof Boileau & Lily & the others. Andy transferred to our college & Ed, the one who stutters, & Dee, signed up for Prof Boileau too. Gene went to work in his fathers furnature busness & Stefanny & Betty decided just to drop out this summer & do pottery down at their pad in Venice. Their fathers will give them money. I will still get my lab money, & it jumped to $2.50 an hour on account of a government grant & I will get 20 hrs a week in. That means I get $42 a week which is plenty. I will still pay ½ the rent which is $60 a mo for my share & Sharon buys all the food & pays the utilitys, & I do most the cooking & the skys the limit on our food budget, so we been eating real good & there's Sharons car, so we got wheels. Prof Boileau's foundation still paying my tuition & next fall I get full *scholarship* on account of my grades. (Man, if the regastrar knowed how I got my A's underneath of Lary at first)

Now for some really big news.

After finals the SDS (me too) took off for Baha Calafornia Mexico & spent the groovyest week on the beach south of Ensanada you coud imagine. I have now been out of the U.S. of A. for the first time. I lyed about my age at the border – oh, by the way, I forgot to tell you I got a fake drivers permit that Andy got me, so it looks like I am 18 instead of 17 which helps a lot. Theyre always asking for our I.D. I cant buy beer, of course, but being 18 I can get in & drink coke & *dance* which if I was 17 I coudent even do that. These *dum* laws!

We were on the beach 5 days. Andy & Ed bought some really good grass at Tiajuana on our way down so we got high evrey night, slept in blankets on the beach, Ed & Sharon are making it very often now, except Sharon is a very shy girl & even tho I am her *best frend* now, we dont talk about who we make it with which is okay with me. Andy had some acid, too, but only him & Betty, who will try *anything* once, had trips. Hers was awful, but Andy gave her a pill that brought her down right away. She cryed for along time after it was over on the beach, then we all went swimming naked & sat around the fire talking & she was okay from then on.

We had long talks about the world & the Problem & what was going to happen this summer (I said L.A. was going to blow up & practicly beleeve it – I have feelings lately about the future, which is something I want to talk to you about, Diary, when we get time) & we all decided we ought to start a colony that was really hip, & leave each other to do our own thing.

But we run out of food & money in 5 days & nobody coud cash a check down there at the village store, so we come home. It felt very good to get home & cleaned up, but *good* to *remember* the groovy tales we had down there underneath the Mexican stars & hear that lovely lanky Dee play her gitar & we all sing.

Wished Dicky Atwater been there, Dicky woud of loved it. He wants to come down here this summer after school. Dicky isent at all dumb but wow, is he a freak out when it comes to school! Maybe he'll be down in August. I hope so. I like Dicky. We wrote each other some this spring, but not much. I dident feel like sending him letters to his house, so stuck notes in Sharons letters a couple times.

Diary, I will try to tell you all the things been happening since I wrote in you last, but there been so much I dont know where to start or even if I can remember ½ of what we been talking & doing.

Well, Sharon is the big Politico of the SDS, Andy the Medico, Dee the Musico, Ed the Bakero (he goes shopping & has bread) & Betty the Garbagio & me, of course, the Cuckoo Cookero. Anyhow, Sharons always getting dispaches from her Uncle Jules in the Senate, who wants her to come to Washingtown D.C. after she graduates next year, & work for him, so the SDS never very far off of politics when Sharons there. We had a trial about War on the beach. Stuttering Ed played LBJ sending 20,0000 troops to Dominican Republic & 50,000 to Viet-Nam (its up to *that* – hope it dosent go any higher or all the SDS going to get drafted & go to war, which *they wont do*) Sharon was the prosecuter & Ed in the witness box, & the rest of us the jury. Sharon clamed in the name of Uncle Jules that LBJ was a dictater bent on making all of South America a weak satalite of the U.S. of A., & all Asia the same, & thats why all them troops. She said Ed (LBJ) a Roman emperer as bad as Ceesar & we ought to fine him gilty. He coudent defend himself because he stuttered. We found LBJ (Ed) gilty as charged & made him crawl naked to the water while we whupped him with palm leaves (not hard) & he stuttered out 'nnno, nnno, nnno!' It sounds kooky now, but was fun.

Diary, besides these wars, the things in the U.S. are awful. I can see now why Dicky – or even Sharon – wants to drop out & its only people like Prof Boileau who keeps them in school at all. If I listed for you what happened this last month you woud understand how Sharon & Dicky & the others feel & why Woody's gone so far out on his kick, & why Andy's high on grass half the time & why Dicky wants to split, & not even out of high school yet. I will list a few.

1 – The FBI thinks the Berkely student stuff that Sharon grooves on so is the fault of the Commys (but the SDS are in on all this underground stuff & know better, how come the FBI so high & mighty dosent know better? Persons like the SDS just dont dig generals & presadents any more, thats the problem, not Commys.)
2 – I saw Truman the other day (like him) & he said some judges on the highest court in Okla. took money for bribes – if so, what can you beleeve in Justice? Nothing!
3 – And Truman said some poor man named Rev Ashton Jones 68 years old spent 8 months & 1 day in jail for trying to go to the 1st Babtist Church in Atlanta with 2 black girls last year. They just now let him out of the pokey, all jacked up. When I told Dee that, she said she never going to a Babtist church again, but start her own church.
4 – Even the people who play cards for fun cheats – the British bridge team. Who cares? But on the other hand, why cheat at *that*? They are dumb to cheat on something so dum.
5 – Lots of KKK weddings with burning crosses in the paper. Ugh.
6 – Still throwing people in jail in Selma & Jackson, Mississippi.
7 – Flunked out only negro in space program. (No flying cats *this* year.)
8 – Only black cop in Bogalusa gunned down. Bombings. 'Deacons for Defense & Justice' is a new black club. Bet you Woodys there. All the SDS want to meet Woody when he

comes home, but ... will Woody want to meet them???
9 – CORE says to the negroes, arm up, if the whites going to gun you down like this. Them Bogalusa 'Deacons' claim they already got hand grenades & machine guns for war. (Woody??) Who needs Viet-Nam for fighting? Ed says if he's drafted, he's going to volunteer for the 'Deacons'.
10 – Marches all over, L.A., New York, Chicago, Alabama. Geo. Wallace is telling the govt. to go-to-hell on segragated schools & the Senate past a law against private armys training for sabotage. Sharon says she's going to ask Uncle Jules what they going to do about the CIA army training against Castro? Is *that* against the law too? (Ed says the CIA a private army & may someday turn against us.)
11 – LBJ's wife starts war on ugliness, Betty said. Betty tends to be mean, so she says 'charity begins at home'. She says LBJ cheated the first time he ever got elected down in Texas, (so they say, anyhow – I dont beleeve it) why shoud we expect any difrent now? Sharon says you have to be a cheater to stay in power. If so, why stay in power? Because its fun, Sharon says.
12 – LBJ says what we need is a Instant Army to keep Castro in his place whenever he springs up in South America.
13 – The GI's in Viet-Nam really in the fighting, not just advisers. This been going on, but LBJ lyes all the time about it. Betty says he's such a lyar she has to find her a new daddy image.

Well, Diary it is the sour 13th of the month & 13 creepy things been happening since I wrote last. I sure cant blame Dicky or Woody or anybody else for revolting. Is the Lord in Charge? Andy says he's going to have to invent a new Lord. Thats why he smokes pot & takes acid. The world is going round & round in my head.

(P.S. I read this over later & it isent very clear. I was about ½ high when I wrote it but I am *not* going the way of Russel & Andy, am going to not freak out on grass so much. Jack woud not like it. It is sily to write in you when I am high. It seems real good at the time, but when I read it over later seems all washed out.) Spare my soul!

June 14, Monday

Woody come back last night. Havent seen him.

June 15, Tuesday

Yes, I seen Woody but he dident see me. Still quivering from it, Diary, I guess I still love that wildcat of a man. He sure looks good, but needs some more meat on his bones. The darling looks older, & he's getting so hansome as he gets older! He's letting his hair grow out like evreybody's doing natural now, & a goatee & still wearing blue denim clothes but got this beautiful white poncho, like linen, all embroydered in difrent colored designs like African that he wears over his shirt. The nice & strong thing is, Woody dont try to dress like a white man any more. For the first time I know for sure he's got something *inside* he's trying to get out which is real, & not just a case of wrath against Whitey. I cant describe it, Diary, except there's something fierce & lovely growing inside Woody that seems to show on his face & in his hot eyes in a way it never did before, it has to do with the way he stands (calm & straight) & the way he looks so dignified at you.

He dident see me, on account of I snuck out as soon as the trouble started. Leona phoned me Woody was back in town with Mr. Sims whose head of the Bogalusa Deacons & they were meeting down at Rev Smiths church. I told Prof Boileau about it, so we all went as part of the field study, but after we got inside Mr. Sims said what he had to talk about wasent for white reporters or white folks altogether. But there we were, Andy & Ed & Dee & Lily & the others with tape recorders & cameras around their necks, & pencils & paper doing their investigation. I seen what was coming & dident want Woody to see it was me brung some of them pushy whites so I split right then. They kicked them out, all right. Sharon & them dident hold a grudge, but Prof Boileau said he counted on me to get the field group into places like that & how come I snuck out? I coudent tell him about Woody, & me not wanting him to see me. How do you explain a thing like that? Maybe I can get Mr. Sims to talk to the white people alone later. Diary, what should I do? I dont know if I want to see Woody. I feel scared of him.

June 16, Wensday

Went to the beach today. Andy & me dident go to Watts with the field group on purpose. They are talking to the black people down there trying to find out how come Watts is like it is. I coud tell them in 1 word. Money. But they woudent understand except maybe Andy but he woudent either, he's white & can always write home for more bread or at least get a bankloan which I coud never do, if I walked in & they figured I was nappy-black. Got high at the beach & lissened to Bob Dylan & The Beatles. The Beatles got a Medal from the Queen & made evreybody mad. Some war heroes turned their medals in when they found out the Beatles got one too. That is like what the Whites will do when they find out guys like Woody mean bisness. They really dont want Woody (or the Beatles) to get medals after all. I dont think getting a medal from the Queen is going to change the Beatles. They got famous just about the time Jack dyed. He sort of gave them something to sing about.

June 18, Friday

Sick in bed. Sharon gone to Watts. I havent been down there since Mon. when we tryed to hear Mr. Sims & saw Woody. Im not very sick, just the sniffels, only Selma to keep me company. Prof Boileau wants to meet Woody, but Diary, Im scared. If they want to meet Woody they should do it on there own.

I see now they're arresting marchers in Alabama & putting them in garbage trucks, there are so many. The L.A. Police wanted to know what Mr. Sims doing in L.A. I wonder if he told them the truth. The truth is, Diary, I am scared of seeing Woody. He is bound to scorn me for living with Sharon & having Prof Boileau down in Watts. Mr. Sims will be on Louis Lomax TV show Sunday. I am not going to interduce Prof Boileau to Woody, he can watch Mr. Sims on Louis Lomax instead, if he's so hot to meet him. Besides, I am sick.

June 20, Sunday

Felt better yesterday (maybe because I knowed I woudent have to go to Watts over the weekend). Just finished watching Mr. Sims on TV. He is pretty good but I coud see he wasent saying all he felt in front of the whites. He did say, tho, as long as theres police brutality & the white supremacy shit everywhere, he wants to start chapters of the Deacons evreywhere for protexion. Lots going on in Miss. Sharon told me she heard about a State Trooper who took a American flag away from a 5-year-old Negro boy marching. I hate that. Not enough they cart them off in garbage trucks. Mr. Sims says the way they get rid of the photographers down there is arrest them *first* for disturbing the peace, so they cant take pictures of what really hapens.

Diary I have decided. I cant be anything else but what I am. If Woody thinks I am white-on-white for coming to live with Sharon I cant help it, & if Prof Boileau ends up thinking Woody is Commy & bad, I cant help that, but *I have decided* tomorrow I am going to find Woody & let Prof Boileau & the class meet him. Prof Boileau is a good man & woudent hurt anybody. I cant help it if he's white.

June 21, Monday

Have decided to stay for a few days at Mama Popes starting tomorrow. Will write soon to tell you why, ect.

June 27, Sunday

Back at Sharons.

What a week! Intraduced Prof Boileau & the group to Woody & Big Ron in Rev Smiths Church on Monday. Woody was very nice, & talked for nearly 1 hr. with us. He is a *terrific* guy. I never saw him so calm & coud he talk to Prof Boileau! Not like some black man to a Prof, not like Truman at the college, but right *across* to him, equal. Woody said he dident have time to spend with the group but said he woud assign somebody to help them see persons they want.

They are so child-like. Andy is a little like poor Russel, of course, always about ½ high on grass, except Andy isnt on any hard stuff (& hope he never does, like poor Russel!), but the rest of them dont understand how careful they shoud be down there. I told Sharon they are down in Watts where a powder keg is about to blow up, but being rich all these years they dont know how some of them hopheads down there woud as plain stick a shiv in poor Ed's gut as look at him, for the $10 they coud get out of his wallet! Woody promised me in secret later to take care of them *this* week & maybe next, but I got to get them out of there or they are in danger. People tired of them white groups coming down doing surveys & nothing ever happening, like Mayor Yorty been haggeling all spring now over who gets to run the gov't. money for Watts, meanwhile nothing happening & the money just laying there. Maybe I am too scared, Diary, but I dont think so, after what Woody told me about the powder keg ready to blow up. All it takes is one heat wave . . .

Spent Thurs nite with Woody over the hole-a-go-go. He told me to quit pot. Malcolm X never used it, nor Muhammad Ali or any other great & good person, & only the weaklings like poor Russel still strung out on stuff, or high on pot. Mama Pope's too old to care about, so if she takes a joint so what? But not the young folks. So, we *dident* smoke any pot, & we *dident* have nearly as good times as we used to, but we had one good fuck that made up for all the rest. Woody getting to be a very pure man, & all that energy he got, when it comes roaring into you all at once like that, enough to set you *absalutely* on fire. God, I love that Woody, diary. I love him so much, & his wild hair & whiskers & that *terrable* look in his big eyes & them clothes he wears with so much dignity, I am so lucky to of knowed him, & him still want to fuck me like that. He coud have practicly anybody in Watts, I think, for the asking, but he spent Thurs, nite with me. I wanted him Friday too & he half promised but was up in Bakersfield or someplace instead.

June 28, Monday

Prof Boileau happy as he can be. Woody assigned a boy to Prof Boileau who goes to USC & wears a regular whitey suit & narrow tie & evreything, & lets Prof Boileau talk to Black Panthers & Deacons & Black Muslims & the other clubs they got going. The thing is, *I* know what Woody thinks about Prof Boileau by assigning Leonard Wolfe (thats the cats name) to our field group, it is like talking to Black Panthers whose teeth all pulled out. I know things happening in Watts what Prof Boileau nor no other white man knows about, but I am not going to tell. Why should they know? They never can, really, & that parts none of their bisness. I only trust & hope by next week the field study finished & we go back to the lab on campus instead.

Diary, in case you wondered what this field study is, it means we do tapes of people talking, & shoot a little 8 mm film, & lots of notes, & the group is broken down into difrent topics. Andy going to write a thing on drugs in the Ghetto. (Poor Russel out on parole getting $20 for an interview a couple times a week, but he needs a lot more than that for his habit.)

Lily doing a thing on language black-talk. (What she dosent know is, how those cats can turn it on & off when they want & are just playing games with her).

Ed & Dee doing a thing on what people eat – how much, & how unbalanced there diet is, coke & animal crackers ect, ect, & trying find out how much proteen the childern get under the age of 4. (I guess it has to do with what happens to your brain)

Well, that's what they're doing, & after they ask enough questions & run enough tape they (we) go back to the lab & analise it, like Woody says, out where we're all safe & clean, & with all the soul-truth left back in Watts. So you can see why Woody makes fun of it. *He* knows that if the black man had the money, thats all he'd need to handle the proteen, drugs, straight talk, ect ect ect, so he thinks these studys all a pile of shit (white mans shit) just to delay the day of freedom, & thats how come the Black Panthers we talk to all had their teeth pulled. I think Woody is only ½ right. I think the way to get the money is play along with Prof Boileau & the govt. Leonard Wolfe is a real copout & Woody knows it. What does that make me? I dont know, but at least I'm a good fuck for Woody, which is something Leonard Wolfe isent.

July 5, Monday

Back at Sharons after a groovy & cool – but painful – 4th of July with Woody & Leona & Big Ron & the others. They chided me a lot about Sharon & Prof Boileau & wanted to know how much I told the Group about how they getting a big fat put-on by Woody & Leonard Wolfe, on how terrable things really are in Watts. I dident tell the Group anything & if there was any put-on it was evreybodys fault, Woody for not letting them know how ready the cats were to kill, in their despair, & Prof.

Boileau for being an Anthro prof yet not able to see the despair while he stood amongst it.

I had no idea how deep & bitter Woody become. I always knowed he was deep & bitter, but when he come back this time from the east he looked so *tough & calm* I thought he wasent bitter any more. What I am trying to say, Diary, that Woody used to be for intragration. Now he isnt. Thats what I mean by deep & bitter. I think I better get the group out of Watts before something happens. I will talk to Sharon & Prof Boileau tomorrow.

But, about the painful 4th, what a national holiday! Woody went up to Denver with Big Ron for two days to the NAACP meeting there & I guess they had a wild one. So much been happening, the NAACP bound to go active soon, or dye, Woody said. Hunderds been locked up in Chicago where Rev. King been called a commy by the Mayor there, & as if that isent enough for the Holiday, over the 4th 30,000 kids went on a turmoil – & on the L.A. Times you shoud of seen the police car that they wrecked, windows smashed, hood sprung, tires cut, Woody says pictures like that can really give you ideas. If some white punks out on a drunk can get away with it, think how justifyed sombody who *really* got a gripe. Especally down in Jackson, where the KKK burned 42 crosses as warnings to blacks.

Woody & me had a super fuck, though, on the 4th after we left Leonas & Big Rons, which was the cool & groovy part of the holiday. I wanted to do *anything* to him (& I meant *any-thing*) but he just wanted to fuck strait, which is okay with me. (Man, is he good!)

P.S. Some blond white girl named June Lindeman is Miss Calif. this year, crowned at Long Beach. I know sombody else who would like to crown her. Me. In the name of all the pretty but nappy-haired girls in Calif. who will *never* win a contest because she isent 100% Anglo.

July 9, Friday

More terrible things, diary. It is Friday & today I *pleeded* with Prof Boileau to finish up the field work in Watts before somebody got hurt. I told him the world going to hurt him & Sharon & the others if he wasent careful. I told them how all this stuff on TV was turning evreybody on, like that sniper from the jungle they had in Honolulu that shot 6 people; & the way they beat up on 4 Indian students (from India) who went to a white rally in Baton Rouge by mistake; & how (worst of all for Watts) L.A. doesnt get its teen-age money this year from the gov't after all on account of Mayor Yorty bickering, & everybody knows it; & only 60 blacks out of 3300 in the Fire Dept.

Like they're all saying, its going to be a *long hot summer* with all those cats on the street, & more than that, I feel it every time they blow up another house in Florida or like when Mr. Sims Deacons got mixed up in shooting 2 white men. Rev King says the L.A. mony for poor people wont help it's too late, but he says, too, the Deacons dont do right by toting guns. What *is* right? I want to be far away, sometimes, when the shooting starts. (Except sometimes I want to be next to Woody so I can share our mingled bleeding blood.)

July 13, Tuesday

Prof Boileau made us all march up to city hall to protest the poverty program which isent getting off the ground. Big deal. There wasent more than 150 in the whole march, dident even slow traffic down.

July 15, Friday

Seen Woody this afternoon intirely by accident at a MacDonalds Hamberger. Diary, my soul itched for him, all my blood drained down to a big blob in my belly. Sharon & me & Andy, then suddenly, Woody, his hair natural, his huge-poka-dot black & white buba shirt cut loose with a T neck to make his shoulders look broad. I think Sharon woudent mind jugging Woody. That cat spent most his time on her, just to taunt me, I think. He knowed what I thought & how my belly went to glue for him. Sharon's all broke up over that Adlai Stevenson dyed yesterday on the street in England, thats all she talked about. Just keeled over, whop!

July 19, Monday

Another week & Prof Boileau *still* dragging us to Watts. Big Rons in Bogalusa with Louis Lomax & Leona sort of worryed. *When will the powder keg blow up?!* Ron phoned & said some honky turned a hose on him. He dam near lost his cool. It only takes *once* to lose your cool & your a dead nigger. The hunky, Ron said, told him 'you need a bath, & even after you clean, you still smell like a nigger.' The hunky dident get arrested, of course, but 2 black girls watching did. 2 more churches gone, burnt. Willie Brewster shot last week dyed today. *It all adds up.* Mama Pope say she thinks she'll leave Watts. The whole town's going to burn down this summer. But where coud Mama Pope go? Not down home, its even worse there. Besides she's only ½ through with that pretty yellow blanket she croshaying for Sharon. Seen it today. Mystic marks threaded through it like orange lightning. Sharon *loves* it. Sharon & her talked about plans to rent a car – not just any old car, but one of them big long black ones like they use for funerals & drive Mama Pope to the ocean, maybe even down to Mexico someday. With

Mama in the front seat where she coud see good, propped up on a cushon. Mama had cooked up some blackeyed peas, but they went sour waiting for us. We shoud drop in *every* day, instead of just when *we* feel like it. Mama hates to have us go. She likes to touch Sharons arm.

July 30, Friday

Diary, thank the Lord & praise be, I finely convinced Prof Boileau to stop going to Watts. And nobody got hurt. I was *sure* sombody going to get hurt, but thanks to that square Leonard Wolfe, we finished up our field study with no blood, thank you dear Lord & thank you, spirit of Jack, who takes care of me & my loved ones thru thick & thin. (Leonard got a little roughed up, but if he hadent of been there, no telling what.)

As you know, Diary, I warned Sharon & Andy & Prof Boileau for *weeks* about parking their cars every day down on Central & fanning out with their recorders & cameras & clip boards like a bunch of spys. Leonard managed to keep us from the really mean cats – the downrite bad assed niggers and mescins who've lost all their manners & just as soon pull a piece or a shiv on you. Now that even the *tame* cats is out of the woods, the really bad-assed chicks & cats have to do even *worse* to show off, thats where the danger is. Leonard bound to make a mistake. Wensday afternoon he arranged for us all to go to a warehouse where some Citazens Patrol met secret to plan which sector to tail cop cars in tonight (they do this all the time now to try to keep the police brutality down, but cant *every* cop car, so just do a sector at a time). They divvy the city up in sectors, & thats what started it.

Some *real* natural cat who I havent seen before, with wild beautiful hair & even tattoos on his cheek dident want their Citazens Patrol Chief to show us the Sector Map, on account of (it turned out) they had a rebellion attack plan marked on it, too, but Leonard claimed Woody give the okay, so this natural cat told Leonard this warehouse wasn't no place for honkeys, black or white, Woody or no Woody. He dident wait around. He had a shiv out right *now* pushing Leonards suit coat belly, & when Leonard said Stop, not to rip his new coat, this cat went ape & pushed even harder & drew blood right through his shirt.

I dont know if I did right, Diary, but I told this cat he dident have any argument from me, & I left. Diary I am a coward. But I also can feel the future all around me & dont *think*. I only *do*. The thing to *do* was not to try & push this bad & wild-eyed cat around at all, but to split.

Thank god Prof Boileau got sense enough to see blood when its drawn, so him & Sharon & the others left almost rite behind me. Plenty scared. Leonard only had the 1 knife mark on his belly, & lucky for that. He moaned he was going to call Woody & tell on this cat, which he did, & Woody said to Leonard, 'Go ahead, Leonard, like I said, nobody going to hurt you on account of your black.'

'Oh yeah?' Leonard said.

'Maybe it was that pin stripe suit your wearing,' Woody said. 'You ever read The Dutchman?' (thats a play where the cat gets made fun of because he wears narrow shoulder suits like Leonard)

'I'm not changing suits for you or anybody else,' Leonard said.

'Then you're on your own, Sport,' Woody said.

That scared Leonard, so he quit working for Prof Boileau (he was getting $100 a week from the college foundation, I found out) & Prof Boileau called the rest of the research off. We got plenty enough to analize anyhow, & thank god no blood spilled, except a drip or 2 of Leonards! Which hardly counts.

Meanwhile I am home flowing enough blood for all. Very hard this time, probly from nerves. Darling Rev King led 50,000 in Chicago on TV yesterday, with another 100,000 watching. But, bad news here in L.A., the poverty program is ruled by hunkeys, not by the poor folks, & *this means trouble.* Mayor Yorty walking on thin ice. They say the city is rich & the money coming in is up, but since they cut back the bus service in Watts last month you better not tell anybody down *there* that.

Well, good news too. Dicky past his makeup course in summer school & will be down in a couple weeks. Will be fun to see Dicky. I will move into Sharons room & he can have my sofa – or shoud I go stay with Andy? No, not while Woodys around, *in case he calls*. Or should I go to Mama Popes? No, for 3 reasons

1 – I am scared of what will happen in Watts.
2 – How coud I get out to the lab every day from there with no wheels?
3 – I woud not see Dicky much if I was at Mama Popes.

No, I will stay here. Glad I am flowing now instead of when Dicky comes. It smells, & we only got 1 bathroom.

July 31, Saturday

LBJ signed Medicare. Now Mama Pope can go to a decent docter free. Flowing.

August 1, Sunday

Andy over. Already high, wanted me to take a joint, did. He was disgusted when he found out I was flowing & said I shoud of told him at the beginning. Sharon come home from out with Dee to a movy & when she smelled grass said if we smoked pot outside the bathroom again, we woud all get busted & if she got busted her uncle would be madder than hell & it would hurt his rep. I dont care about pot, really, now that Woodys give it up. But, there's no call atall for Andy or Sharon to get disgusted with me. Life is Love. Still a little high, I guess. Poor Russel got busted again last week & its the cooler for a good long time for sure, now. He's out on bail for a few days, but all that does is help him stay strung out on stuff a little longer.

August 2, Monday

Lab. all day hearing the coolest tapes with Lily, who's figuring out what black talk really is from these crazy cats she recorded. She cant understand it, so I am getting $2.50 a hour transalating. Diary, do you dig? $2.50 a hour! I woud sure rather do this all my life than work at Macdonalds or hussel. Paper says everybody in Calif. getting richer by 7% a year. Bet Woody isent.

August 3, Tuesday

Lab. Talked to Lily about how in Miss. they put you in jail & fine you if you have more than 1 baby without a husband. She dident believe it, but Truman showed me in the paper the other day where 98 been arrested for it. (We run into him in Watts. Dig.) The law was past in 1964. Lily is nice, but very hunky in her views, which she inherated from her folks so you cant blame her &, lissen to this, Diary: she thinks just because most black girls pelvic bone is shaped difrent than most white girls (which Prof Boileau says is true) that she can trace this to black talk versis white talk being heredatary. I shoudent of, but I told her I woud believe it when chicks started talking out of their pussy, but not before. That shocked Lily, which I like to do to see her color change.

August 4, Wensday

Well well well. They elected a black girl Miss New York State. Maybe I got a chance after all for rose quean. Her name Gloria Jon & she 22, with 36–22–35. I am 36–23–32, which means I got to bild up my poor boney little hips. But rather be skinny than have big oil bags. More transalating.

August 5, Thursday

Diary, I shoud laugh at this like Woody does now, & get a kind of black joy like he does, but I cant. It stabs me. *I* know I will never be Rose Quean or Miss Calif with my skinny little butt & all, & to think I ever woud was only a game I been playing with you, Diary. But that poor Gloria Jon who they made Miss N.Y. got a letter stripping her title. It was from the hunky in charge & it said, 'I never expected a Negro to win, & this is not the image that the N.Y. state Pageant wants to foster.'

I leave it to you, Diary, & to the spirit of JFK in gods *fair* heaven to decide whether the hurt & the hate I feel is right, or if I shoud laugh? It makes me burn, & *want* to burn, baby, burn, sometimes like Woody says when him & Ron get *feirce* with people they talk to & say things gentle Sharon and Prof Boileau never of heard & would never want to, let alone people like poor Lily, who never did get over about my jibe about pussys & her talk project, which I never should of made.

I guess I will not enter the Orange County Miss World Contest this year after all (ha, ha, ha).

August 6, Friday

More lab & nearly finished transalating for Lily. I give her a few wrong transalations from black talk just to fool her, but shoudent of. I tole her a 'jackleg preacher' is one with a limp (not one without a church), and she claimed a 'piece' meant ass, or like she said, 'Body', not a gun, so I let her believe it, but she's wrong, and when it come to 'jugging' (which is *really* ass) i told her (very meanly) it meant to blow music out of a gallon wine jug. I am sorry, I just felt like not helping anybody for a while. LBJ says there only 9 out of 4,000 Navy trainees at Annapolis who is negro, & wants to know why? If he wants to know why, let him ask Woody. Woody can tell him why.

Money. Money gets you everywhere, including into that place.

Today Sharon & me bought tickets to the *Beatles*, right here at the Holywood Bowl ($7 each!) for *Aug. 29 Remember that date.*

August 8, Sunday

Lord, has it been hot! Over 100° in the apartment & its usally way cooler out here than Watts. Must be a real sizzler down there. Mama Pope ought to have a air cooler at her age.

Sharon gone all weekend to get Dicky up at Monteray & see her folks. Andy come around, but I said no. I dont feel like pot, or *it*. Only 1 more week of labs & then *1 month off*. I plan to just lay around the beach & maybe read some books for fall term. I got money now & good friends & evreybody has to suffer the heat, so I cant complain about that. Hope Mama Popes okay. Old people dye in the heat & she's been very blue about this sumer. She's withering down, old woman. I wonder if I will ever be old, & bilt like cobwebs.

3 weeks from today, *The Beatles* in person.

August 9, Monday

Wached the Miss U.S. of A. Beauty Contest from Long Beach on TV. I will be as old as Mama Pope before they ever have a black girl on. Sharon called. She will be back Wensday with Dicky. Had to walk the 6 blocks to the Lab today. More translating. HOT!

August 10, Tuesday

Lonsome without Sharon. Dident think I woud be. Nearly had Andy drive me to Watts, but woud of probly had to fork out for him, & dident want to, nor dident want him driving high. Sharon promised to teach me to drive. I am old enough, but cant picture doing it. Heat still on, 7th awful day. I am getting strange shivers in all this heat like standing up on the edge of a boiling volcano which it is about to bubble up & then the sides cave in. Dicky due with Sharon tomorrow. I am going to sleep absalutely naked tonight & still bet the sheet sweats. Selma Kitty just lays around panting. Hardly worth it to go to the beach its so hot there, & so many persons.

August 11, Wensday

Afternoon Dident even go to school today it was so hot. Laid around & played with kitty. Picture of that girl June Lindeman who is the blonde Miss Calif in the paper. Felt real horny & wanted Woody real bad or even Andy. Diddaled myself. Shoudent of, I suppose, but who is to lose? Dont have pimple trouble like I used to. Makes you forget the heat & always has made cramps easier, tho no cramps today, just horny. In a little while Sharon & Dicky will get here. Feel pooped out from the diddaling & the heat & the near-sick excitement I feel about Dicky coming & the volcano bubbling sick & hot & wild. Will stop now & clean the pad up. (clean sheets & maybe to the laundromat, but *so* hot) Cold shrimp & beer for dinner tonight. Maybe Dicky will get a little drunk & funny.

August 28, Monday

Dear Diary
Oh! . . . i cant write in you to tell you . . .

Wensday

Dear Diary
—I will try in you tomorrow.

September ?

Now i shoud tell you about Mama . . . but cant. will try again.

September 11, Monday

Dear Diary
Help me to get aholt of myself! One whole month past & *life must go on.* No matter what. Pray all night to give me strenth so tomorrow I can finely tell you . . . the truth, which even now so hard to stand.

September 12, Sunday

We shoudent of gone down to Watts. I knew it all the time, & *had* a *feeling*. But Sharon wanted Dicky to see the ghetto in a heat wave for his own good. My shakes told me to stay away, but Sharon & Dicky so innocent they lead such rich lives they dont see death even when its starring right in there eyes – & the thing is, Death seemed not to see them, either.

Now I can tell it. Hot tears & quavering hand, but . . . That nite we had shrimp & beer like I said, it was a Wensday, I think, but they tired from driving from Montaray & it was H-O-T so we dident go out, just layd around talking & playing some sides, Otis Redding – Dicky brought some new albums, Sonny and Cher, Joan Byez, ect.

The riots started that night, but dident amount to much – somebody got arrested & a crowd made the troopers let them go, but this has happened before so I dident think anything about it, nor did the TV make much out of it, except the *general* spooks that made my bones creak & feel weak.

Of course Sharon & Dicky wanted to go to Watts to see Mama, & all, but it was *just too hot* to try it Thursday morning so we went to the beach, but just as hot there. About 10 or 11 Thursday nite we all laid out sweating in the pad with salt burning our skin left over from the beach, when Sharon said lets go down to Watts now to see the action. I said no, afraid for them & – which I was not smart enough to see then, 10 p.m. Thursday is only *2 hours* away from *Friday the 13th* which has always been a very touchy day for me as you know, Diary. But my mind clouded like Mama Popes ball is clouded now by fire, partly because Dicky was on the sofa & me laying naked thinking about him in Sharons other bed & her naked too.

But whatever the reason, as the hour of Fri. the 13th approached we found ourselves in Sharons green MG, me in back, headed down Central avenue, & no sign of riot around at all. We found out later the cops already blocked some streets off, but reading about it later, or being in Police Central, isent like being *there* in the battelfeild at all. Same old Thrifty Drug on the corner, the liquer store, the furnature store, & junk cars in all the vacant lots. The only difrence was, as I think back, not so many cats on the streets, & those who was, clustered in gangs, instead of spread all out like usal – except for that, & the hot, it was like all the nights I ever walked Central which is plenty, for errands both good & bad. Sharon parked her MG (that dear car now burned completely to a crisp, but her daddy already got her a new one from the insurance, but midnite blue, not green).

Anyhow, it was still & heavy, & I heard sirens 2 or 3 streets over, but that happens all the time in Watts so who lissens? We went through the spooky alley between the stores to dear Mama Popes house. I told Dicky not to touch the link fence, & to open the latch with just 1 finger, because the old witch lived here & dident like us stealing her avacados. Oh, we was so smarty & having fun! Kissing the white lion on the way in, & all.

She was up. Johnny Carson on, but she not watching, instead she's in a trance over the cristal ball, that red shawl on her head & silver earrings swaying. I started to open the screen door, but Dicky layed one of his hands on my arm, so we jest watched. Dickys eyes glowed smokey, drawn by the site of old Mama Pope, so stooped in red like a dryed flower setting in them wornout old wool slippers, starring into the ball on the table, while Johnny Carson flickered light & dark on the wall.

Finely Mama Pope said 'Come on in' without looking up like she always does. 'Foolish childern,' she said, 'What you dears doing down here on this night of Death. It's too late for River Jordan. Too late to get ready. You got to get dressed at *home* before you come out on the street, cause if you don't when you get out on the street without no clothes, they'll arrest you & take you to jail. You all dressed up for Death? It's too late to get dressed up, Childern, too late for heaven & glory. When Death wants to, he'll find you.' Then she calmed some, but wouldn't leave the ball, and tears fell.

I tryed to intraduce Dicky to Mama Pope. Sharon said she come to show him her new yellow blanket. I put on the water & found some camomile tea. But Mama woudent budge from the ball. Sharon's blanket layed almost done over the sofa, so pretty she held it up to the light from the ball so the orange lightning showed for Dicky. She tryed to hug Mama thanks, but Mama stayed stiff.

Sharon wanted to know about Mr. Adlay Stevensons soul, & about next times governers & stuff like that but Mama coudent tell her. I know now what it was, she seen death in the cristal ball & coudent keep her old eyes off it. And who coud. 'What *you* want, youngster?' she asked Dicky.

Dicky never lost his cool. He never does. Most 15 year olds woud of tyed up & coudent answer Mama, but Dicky said in his soft voice just as unhurryed as he coud be, 'Are those sirens good music or bad?'

'Good for some & bad for some,' Mama said.

'What about for Sharon & Trixie & me?'

Mama looked in the ball. Her face shrunk, her eyes littler than they used to be, with the sheen gone. 'Get out of here, all you 3 childern, quick.' I never heard her talk so harsh. 'You hurry out where Death cant find you.' Mama's look got through us all. My bones shook & went cold. The sirens stopped. Now I smelled smoke in the air – raw smoke, not just left-over smog. I didnt want to go out, but afraid to stay. I *seen* Death in Mama Pope's eyes as plain as day, like dolls eyes stuck so they wont close. 'Go!' So we split, out past the gate. Smoke curled down, & fire in the next block cast pink flickerings on the back wall of Thrifty Drug. Something big on fire. We panicked for the car, but the alley jammed all of a sudden full of cats coming at us with knives & guns & bottle bombs stuffed with rags from god knows where, niggers gone completely fool-ape looking for blood. They smelled like gas. Just kids, except the natural cat in front I remembered from the one who stabbed Leonard Wolfe, a bone on his forehead & tattoos on his face. That cat gone absalutely out of his skull with fire & hate. We run the other way but they cornered us against a junk car. Poor Sharon so blonde & pale.

'Let us go, Man,' I said but like he dident hear. The younger ones hipnotized by that bone in his hair. He said, 'Get the whites.' Thats when I stood in front of Sharon & poor Dicky. The cat said, 'who you a soul sister of? Them or us?'

'Both,' I said.

'You caint be both.'

I said, 'These folks down here on my fault, they been trying to help us. We just come from Mama Popes, so look out.'

'*They* caint help us,' the cat said. 'Who you soul sister to?'

I said, 'Mama Pope have the hex on you, if you hurt us. She

told us you were out here, & shes gonna work roots on you if you hurt us. If you use those things on us your going against Mama Pope – all of you – & she'll bad mouth you the rest of your lives. You know what her hex can do. She's a witch. You little boys want to be hexed from now on? If you hurt us, you going to get it *forever*.' I said to Sharon & Dicky, 'Lets go. They wont stop us, or God going to come down & strike them dead.'

This natural cat with the bone didnt budge, but the little ones managed to scare enough so they parted & we strolled past poor mama's fence, with a last look at the lion, back of the bildings across the yards, trying not to run & show panic. The flames made evreything red & bright. Nearly to the street, the cat hollered, 'She's a liar, she's a dirty white nigger. Go get her.' So we ran. 'Burn, Baby, Burn!' they screamed even the littelest. We made it to the street but a gas bomb hit Sharons car & it blew up, & you could hear zings of bullets. Seemed like the whole street on fire, & crowds of cats running like molasses. I dont know how the bullets missed us. Dicky got that bloody graze & blood all over his legs but he dident holler or even feel it at the time. Cop cars lined up at the end of the block. We run toward them, Sharon & Dicky ahead, me behind to keep a line between them & that ape-fool cat, though I never ever knew if he come round the corner from the alley. I fell down. You can't tell whats going on, but in your mind you hear it all in slow motion. All the sounds went away except the voice of a cop who said over a bullhorn, 'Get that black bitch.'

The bullet ripped through my left shoulder. The cops run out in a ring around Dicky & Sharon. I heard the cops holler, 'We got her!' Then Sharon screamed & Dicky shouted for them to save me, but the cops dragged Sharon & Dicky behind their car, Dicky dripping blood, & to the white ambulance.

I knew what happened right away. The Man thought I was chasing Sharon & Dicky so they winged me. I layed in the street bleeding all over my black & purple striped shirt, trying to keep it off my new pink stretch-pants, & hurting. The Man all had their guns pointed at me. Something burned fast & fierce back of Thrifty Drug. Mama's full of flame. Oh, terrible!

Mama Pope & Russel both dead.

Yes, dead.

30 people dead (27 blacks) who when I last wrote in you alive & moaning the heat was too much. & now? Some in heaven like Mama Pope but where is Russel tonight, Diary, roasting in the hell he helped make for hisself on dope, & then the poor man run out like a frenzyed madman across Central Ave hurling a gasoline bomb only to get cut down by the machine guns of the soljers. Dead, not a chance.

Thank the Lord it was over quick for Mama. The sudden flare where her house ought to of been. I crawled between 2 stores on the far side & cryed. I woud rather of gone to the Man than back to my own people but they woudent let me. I hated to dye. Paying for my terrable sins. Even Woody woud of let me dye that night for my sins.

Then the Man had to pull back. Gangs all over throwed coke bottle gas bombs through store windows. The furnature store exploded & people gray with smoke ran in & out of the shroudy window hauling things they coud carry. My shoulder ached now. I crawled behind the stores down amongst some dirt & old tires & bedsprings, & then into the back seat of that junk car & passed out.

& Mama Pope, what am I going to do without her? Death come so terrable to Mama, burned up in her little cottage back of the store, not a chance to excape, & my fault for not helping or being with her at the last, the poor old woman who must of seen it all in her cristal ball which made it just that much worse – too worse to stand – while the flames licked around her old house & tree, & her sofa, & Sharons lovely new yellow destroyed blanket, & finely her red shawl & slippers themselves & the old flesh – oh! Diary! Too terrable to relate. My tears wet your pages like they wet them for Jack's head shattered asunder. Come back? No. Nothing will come back, nor no one, not Jack, not all the black men dead from crule crimes over many years, not the assasins bullet or the soljers bullet or the licking flames turned loose by blackmans bombs can ever go *back* & undo their hurts. Their hurts stay as long as I have mind to remember. I will *never* forget, & this vicious scar on my shoulder will always remain to remind me of the worst days I ever spent.

For now I know what its like to get shot with a bullet & have a scar which will never go away. But Dear Lord who protects us all against eternal death, my misery & my scar is nothing compared to the final misery of Mama Pope & poor dead Russel.

It is now way into Sept., a month after I last wrote you. Poor Mama. She loved Sharon, & so good to me though no blood. & Sharon & Dicky & me, too, might just as well have been there when the bomb burst on her shingles, except you, Dear Lord, & the spirit of Jack, watched out for us & sacraficed the old to save the young.

Woody in jail with a thousand others, but Big Ron free to carry on the work. Leona picked up, but let go, but Beverly out on bail. I coud list all my friends & over ½ of them has been arrested by Cheif Parker & his goons – or dead, like poor Russel. Yet who is to say whose falt? Should we burn the city down to make up for all the pain? I dont know, Diary, all I know is, Sharon & Dicky alive. Dickys bullet wound just a grazing one but oh, how it bled, so much worse than mine, & Sharon, my friend, without a scratch, to do good in the years ahead.

Well, Diary, I am absalutely pooped out & cannot write any more. Shoulder aches. If you want to read any more about the riots, how many hurt & dead & arrested & how many million $ $ $ $ up in smoke its still all theyre talking about in the newspapers & TV. It went on from Wensday nite, with a lull Thurs, Thurs nite, all day Fri, Fri nite when it got the worst, out of control *Sat, Sat nite*, Sun, & fizzled out Mon. They still had 3000 Gard in town a week later. This wasent no riot, this was cival war, its been going on for nearly 10 years now & will range worse & worse for 10 more, mark my words, Diary. I know it so clear. My bullet wound is here to tell me when my mind grays over the sad truth.

Father Devine dyed yesterday. He was 100.

September 14, Tuesday

Tomorrow we leave for Montaray. Shoulder still very sore but thank you, Lord, the bone only *touched*, & no infection set in. Sharons new car has a removable bubble instead of a soft top – which means when you are rich, & your car burns up, you dont lose your car, you get a better one. But why shoud I be sour, when Dicky is so sweet. I guess he brings out the witch in me who wants him (I am telling only you, Diary, since he only 15 & rich & all, & Sharons brother. He lets his blond hair grow very hip, & it curls over his neck like pictures on princes.) And he wears a very beautiful smile. I guess its his innocence that turns me on – I feel *safe* in it, since I am so un-innocent & such a crum myself.

Sharon & Dicky found me at General Recieving Hospital & when they did, had me hauled to one out here where you dont have to lay down in the halls & where they treat you nicer.

At nearly daylite Friday I come too, in the old car back of the stores, but so stiff I coudent move. My clothes wrecked. All I coud smell was smoke & death & old tires & my own caked blood. My pink pants absalutely wrecked. People ran around back of stores carting loot all nite. Some little boys found me, but thank goodness not the same ones under the spell of that fool-ape cat. I told them to go get Big Ron or Woody, but they run away & never come back. Thats the way it is in war.

Well, by broad daylite I managed to crawl & stagger to the edge of the blocked-off part, & a couple good ladys helped me to where the Gard stood with their guns. I coudent believe they woud shoot a hurt woman, & I was right. The Gardsmen treated me very tender, just boys like at the college, only big green helmets that made there faces look skinny. I got took in a police ambulance & I guess I shoudent be anything but plain *glad* I excaped, but at General Receiving they were rough & surley & mean, like they been working all night, & it was *my* fault I had a police bullet in me. Not in me, actally, it went clean through the fatty part of my shoulder down by the arm pit. I must of had my arms up pleading when they fired. I am *so* lucky. 6 inches into my body from here, & my hart woud be dead & you, diary, ended. 6 little inches.

I laid for 2 days in the hospital hall. Some nurses swore & hated all the blacks in there. I pissed on my cot. I coudent help it, they had me shot so full of drugs I dident hardly know it & too weak to get up, & some hunkey docter (been up 2 or 3 nites, probly) really chewed me out & said 'Go ahead, piss all over the public dole, thats what you was raised to do' – stuff like that.

Then Sharon & Dicky come. They coudent find me that first night on account of Dicky to the hospital & Sharon with him. They went back Friday but coudent get in the area blocked off by sniper fire. Fri. afternoon they started in on the hospitals (& the morgue – ugh!) but so many persons in & such a mess, no names at the desk, until Sat. nite they found out where I was but coudent have me transferred till Sunday. In war, it takes that long. But I had faith. True, I wondered where they was, but when Sharon showed up (they woudent let Dick come up, with his bandaged leg & only 15) I just blubbered & she hugged me (gently) & kissed my face with her warm lips, lovely Sharon.

Well, that was that. 5 days in the hosp. to make sure gangrene wouldent set in & no infection, then back home. Meanwhile, little by little word come about Woody, Big Ron, poor dear Russel, Leona, Beverly and – of coarse – Mama Pope, whose name we read in the paper & found out that way. Burned to the ground. I cry, writing it.

Now I got Mama's cristal ball:

A very strong *thing* in me told me, when I got well enough to think, that I should ought to have the ball. I told Sharon how much it meant. Sharon of course can move heaven & earth when she wants, her fambly's so high up, so when she found out how I wanted it, she called to her daddy, & after that all she needed was to show up at the local precinct & got a cop car with 2 cops to gard her, to go down after the riots & find the ball. It was there, fell amongst the black ashes of the cottage, where nobody bothered to look. Now I got it with me to keep always. It is still clear, *in between* the crinkly lines that go to its core from fire, & you got the feeling of looking deep into it, like poor

Mama done, though from a short ways off it looks clouded gray. I hope. I hope. You know what I hope, Diary, that I can learn to plum its depths like Mama could, in memory of her power & wisdom.

So, tomorrow to Montaray. I am a big hero with Sharons folks, of course. Mrs. Atwater phoned & made me talk to her so she could invite me, with her own voice, to Montaray, so I knowed I woud be wellcome & not just what Sharon & Dicky told me. Sharon & Dicky told their mamma & daddy that I saved their lives, & even Uncle Jules talked to Sharon. Him & LBJ sent 2 real high guys out here to find out about the riots & Sharon helped take them around. I coudent, of course, being in bed. They offered to bail Woody out, but Woody cant get out on bail, the way they got him charged. I guess they blame him for nearly evrything – or woud like to. He probly's going through hell now, in Chief Parkers Palace jail, but I hope he dont get messed up too bad, & hope he gets a bunk to sleep on, & dont get in with a bunch of hunkys who take it out on him. But Woody is tough, & these are tough times. I wonder what hapened to that fool-ape cat with the bone?

Well, here I am rambeling on just like I used to & vowed never again. So much happened this month I cant start to say it all – I guess the Beatles was here, but $14 in tickets down the drain. Nobody even thought of them. The Congress all of a sudden doubling poverty funds, of course, & Chief Parker blaming the State Patrol & the State Patrol blaming the Gov. & Gov. Brown blaming Mayor Yorty & him blaming the Gard & the Gard blaming Chief Parker. I really got to laugh (if it dident hurt to!). Woody said it once & for all: MONEY.

But – I am invited to the Atwaters as a hero. Goodbye for now, Diary. Love you very much.

September 15, Wensday

Montaray:

I brung you along, Diary, & the cristal ball. I will write in you a little at a time at night. Montaray is *lovely*, green trees all over & I can hear the ocean from my bed beating its waves against the craggy white rocks. I am on the 3rd floor of this gray stone *cassell* whose windows have teeny panes all difrent shapes snuggeled down in super smooth candystripe sheets in a huge bed all to myself & 4 pillows, for piling up to read, or hugging, if you feel lonesome up under the roof. They are pillows full of duck feathers that dont get lumpy. A whole fambly could live in this 1 room if it had to. I am a princess.

Sharons mother is *groovy* with gray hair before her time, but the kind of streaky gray you see on models, not on old ladys like Mama Pope. She is ammaculate from her hair to her low heels shoes that look almost Mary Janes but so classy. She talks like shes from England (but isent). She kissed me on the cheek when we come in & keeps calling me 'my dear'. Sharons daddy quiet but nice. I woud almost like to sit on his lap. He smells like leather chairs & shaving lotion, & wears a soft sweater underneath of his coat. He has a *pipe organ* bilt into the house, with a separate room for the pipes that make absalutely *frankenstine* music you can hear through all the walls. Mr. Atwater plays the organ & can even fix it hisself. Sharon says hes always tinkering & its down for repairs ½ the time. His hobby.

Their little brother Augie is cute. His head is big like a babys. He wears a little coat to dinner like his daddy. Very serious, with them gray eyes always on you. He wants to hang around my room, but Mrs. Attwater said no, I was tired. Which I am, & sent him to his own room on the 2nd floor. Dicky & Sharon have their rooms there too that nobody uses when they are away, just always ready for them when they come home. They are asleep now.

Goodnite. Too much to tell.

Raining & blowing outside, but cozy in my bed in the cassell in the green forest on the ocean shore.

September 16, Thursday

Servants & servants (& Im not 1 of them) every time you turn around. They have a soul sister cook in the kitchen & a woman who waits table & a man who is dressed in a suit & is in charge of the whole house & 2 girls with German (Swedish, I guess) acsents who do the upstares & laundry. Then a jap gardner who doesnt live here, but spends 3 days a week *ju*st on this place alone.

Walked on the beach & rocks this morning between rain showers. Arm still in a sling. Sharon lets me use all her clothes (she has *tons* of them up here left over from when she used to wear what her mother wanted. I can take back all I want, to keep. I wore a groovy brown leather coat today & a little leather hat to match with a fringe of fur underneath the brim & some olive riding pants & short boots. We can ride horses if we want to, but I got out of it with my sore arm.)

This house, you dont walk right in the front room from the porch, you walk in a big hall first 2 storys high with a huge thing hanging down with about 50 lights on it looks like candels, & all around the hall balconys where people can look down as you walk in with a big starecase & dark railing slick & curved. Dicky said him & Sharon use to slide down it.

This aft. we went to town where the fish boats come in & had a hamberger out over the water. *Zillions* of gray & white sea-gulls. Jazz festival starts tomorrow. Rex Stewart is playing trumpet, & I told Sharon I will get her to meet him (hope he remembers me from my stepdaddy). I am meeting billionares here & intraduced as the Atwater hero. Everybody here is a awful lush, but havent smelled any pot. Wish I had some for bedtime. Dickys scared to keep it around the house. At dinner tonite, Dicky told me with his eye signals which fork and knife to use. Last nite I goofed up. If your not sure, to work your way from the outside in. Mr. Beeg, who runs the house, at dinner has a silver dust pan scraper to take crums off the tablecloth, & when its over puts the candels out with a silver thing. You get a clean napkin with every meal & they throw it into the wash even if you leave it folded, like I did last night. Dicky & Augie say no, use it & leave it crumpeled when your through. At lunch we ate on the stone patio where high glass keeps the wind off, & the girls windex the glass from spray so you can see out. They let me sit looking out to the water, which is rough & with 'white caps' on it like dashes of soapsuds, because they see it all the time & used to it, but Im not. Diary, this is a mansion, not a house.

September 17, Fri. Night

Late, late, late.

Heard Dizzy Gillespy *and* Louis Armstrong, *and* Rex Stewart tonight play 'Boy Meets Horn' his most famous one. They have the festival in a big horse corral with a stage at 1 end & seats around. Mobs of people. Got Sharon to meet Mr. Stewart & he remembered me but said I have sure growed up. Got Dizzy & Louis autographs & give them to Dicky. Augie dident go, he's too little to care about jazz. I will tell you about him some day. He will be 10 next week & we will stay for his birthday. His eyes is hazy gray, & you just cant quit looking at them. They haunt you.

Am pooped. I get to sleep in all day if I want tomorrow, but Dicky wants to take me to Carmel which is a famous town. He dosent have a drivers permit yet but they let him drive on this drive called a Seventeen Mile Drive that goes right past the Atwaters with gates on both ends. To get in, you got to live on the Seventeen Mile Drive, or know somebody, or else pay. Uncle Jules migt be out here for Augies birthday & on other bisness, hope to meet a *real senetor*.

September 19, Sunday

Jazz festival was something else this weekend. Yesterday John Handy & last night *Duke Ellington*. Fun to see them, but I had enough Jazz for a while. They have a pop festival in the spring, Beatles, ect, wish I coud see that instead.

Well, Sun. nite. Midnight. Wind in the pine trees & the salt spray dancing in the air, but me cozy on the 3rd floor & Sharon said I coud have *all* her clothes if I wanted & her folks will send them by a package. Not really all, of course, but just about anything I want. Dicky shows people his bullet wound some, but dosent like to. Its just a skinslash across his leg. I dont show mine because in a sling, but Sharon makes me show Mama Pope's cristal ball around like a souvaner.

Getting tired of talking about Watts. They are very nice people but want to know all about not just the riot night, but Mama Pope where she come from, & step daddy & my own moma. A man here tonite laughed & said 'what a fambly tree!' Mr. Attwater give him a shut-up glance, but he made me sick. Diary, I woud be fooling you as well as me if i dident say why I am here. I am their showoff from Watts & must pay the price. Woody warned me. Well, the price is O.K., I woud rather be here than tight broke on Central, I will pay the price. They found out tonight Uncle Jules cant come for Augies birthday. Sharons folks actally know Jacky Kenedy & someday . . . who knows? might my dream come true? They said now that she is out of mourning she's going to lots of partys, but you dont hear much about it. The only persons who get in the paper are either the Presadent (he has to) or persons way lower down than the Atwaters. The Atwaters always doing things, & *what a phone bill* they must have, talking to the French Ambassador or to somebody in defense all the time. Mrs. Atwater is Uncle Jules sister. They are very powerful. But very nice to me. Sharon & Dicky wont dress up for dinner which makes Mrs. Atwater mad, but nothing she can do.

Mr. Atwater doesnt say much, but we had a nice talk setting

in a window seat looking over the ocean this afternoon. He's the only one who isnt always bringing up Watts. He told me about his granfather. His granfather help bring the railroads out. He asked me what courses I took in school. He is 1 of the first persons I ever met who asked me that. I think he is a little scared of his wife. I wanted him to play on the pipe organ again, but he said he usally only plays when she's gone.

September 20, Monday

Sharon went horse back riding with some old friends this afternoon, so Dicky & me went down the beach after he got back from school. There are seals on the rocks & pelacans all over the place. Including their shit. Dicky showed me caves underneath their house by the beach. Dicky wants to fuck me I can tell, but doesnt know exackly how to start. He had a hard on today in the cave. I can amagine what Mrs. Atwater woud do if I let him. That would be the end of me a hero. *Krrrrrp*, off at the neck! I better not let him, but he is nice & I like him a lot. He is skinny but quite strong. His curly blond hair used to be down to his shoulder, but they made him cut it off at school & his neck all white where it used to be. He's always rubbing the new bristly stubble on his neck. It itches. I rubbed it for him. I told him to do good in school or they'd get you for it later. The longer you do bad, the worse they can get you. Dicky only wears levis, which his mother just hates. Mr. Atwater never seems to go anywhere to work, but he seems to young to be finished with it.

September 21, Tuesday

The way their money rolls in! Augies Birthday tonight. He got his first bike, but he isent the athaletic type. What he got that he liked better was a great big world (I mean *really* big, about 3ft.

across) lighted from the inside on a beautiful wooden stand, & a set of World Books for his room.

The Atwaters try not to be showy with their money, so thats all they give him, but he *was* cute. He kissed everybody at the table for their presents. (I give him a minature cristal ball – just a big clear marble, really, since he likes to hold Mama Popes ball) & the naibors give him savings bonds & toy machine guns & tanks & stuff.

Sharon said Augie gets $3,000 every birthday in money, & has since he was 1, to keep from losing all the fambly money in taxes when somebody dyes, they start giving it to their kids as fast as they can, up to what the law allows each year. Augie already has $30,000, Dicky $45,000 & Sharon over $60,000, plus interest. Plus a bunch of things that shows they own parts of companys. By doing it this way, the money stays in the fambly. Jack F. K. & his brothers & sisters all got $1,000,000 when they was 21, Sharon said.

September 22, Wensday

Augie & Dicky up in my room before dinner getting me to look at Mama Popes cristal ball. Augie used his, too. We all set on my bed doing Yoga. Dicky wanted to play around but Augie dident notice, I think. 10 is sort of young for somebody rich & innocent like Augie to know when persons want to play around. He looked in his ball. He pretended to see the future. He said when his mom & dad went to heaven he woud bring them back as angels. He said he woud take Sharon & Dicky & me around the world in his own airplane. Dicky said he woud jump out, but Augie said he woud dive down & catch him before he hit the ocean underneath. Then I read Mama's ball & saw dim things in it about me & Dicky but Mrs. Atwater come in so we stopped.

Back to L.A. tomorrow morning. I told Dicky, if he liked me, do good in school this year. He said they coud always yank him out & put him in a private school where everybody pass if they wanted, like the rich can do, but Dicky says his mama wants them to go to public schools so when they get in politics later the people will think theyre plain folks & vote for them. He promised to make me write, but doubt if I will with Mrs. Atwater getting the mail first. She talked about Jacky K tonight, said Jacky was whooping it up at a club in Washingtown D.C. now she's out of morning. Said she was with somebody named Killer Joe, but I dont believe it. I think Mrs. Atwater is bugged living out here & wishes Mr. Atwater had more get-up-&-go when it come to politics, so they coud live in Washingtown D.C. where Uncle Jules is.

September 25, Saturday

Back home. Sign up for school Monday. Everything the same, naibor fed Selma-Kitty & she was here fat & sassy when we got back glad to see us. Sharon out with the SDS tonight but I'm tired, maybe the curse early. I guess Mrs. Atwater was right about Jacky. In the paper today she was the star at a big party in Boston. Here is what they ate at the party:

200 lbs lobsters
60 gallons soup
840 lbs of veal
50 lbs of soul
28 boxes belgium endive (?)
6 cases carrots (they could keep them)
90 flaming souffles
20 cases champain
15 cases wine
15 brandy
9 scotch
9 burbon
6 rye
2 vodka
6 gin

October 1, Friday

Poor Woody's in for it now! They sent him back east on some charges. Ron says he probly'll get a year maximum. Ron says dont write him, he's only allowed so many letters, & every one he gets they hold against him.

Poor U.S. of A. They let another hunky go in Alabama for killing some civil rights worker from the north. Claimed the worker kissed a 'nigger girl' so they killed him. The jury took an hour to find the killer not gilty.

Letter from Dicky. Like. He likes me.

October 2, Saturday

Am I loaded with clothes! Sharons trunk come today. I cant start to tell you all, diary, but I got 10 times more than I ever had & all such pretty & fine cloth. Wools, cottons, silk, leather, fur, lattice-work swim suits, pale green linen, slipover jackets, puff sleeve pink blouse, sleeveless shifts, silk prints, trench coat in double organdy, panti-legs, two-tone colored stockings, fake fur ocelot sleeveless coat reversable to camel-wool, long sleeve mulberry shift with rolled collar, cape-coat in black & white checks, brown lace cocktail dress (spanish style, dropped torso trumpet skirt with a rose-on-the-waste), white bead silk chiffon, navy & wheat colored striped knit with belted overblouse, matching stripe hose, heels heels heels, orange turtle neck sweater & hood to match, a harem costume in pink organdy and sequined pink & black blouse above, ect. ect. ect! What in the *world* did one girl (even rich) do with all those things? Give them to *me*, that's what!

The SDS want me to get a sewing machine & make really groovy costumes out of them. I don't know. I think I would rather just have the clothes, they are such good quality, & like new. All I have to do is shorten the skirts & let out the darts on some dresses. (Sharons only 34 bust).

October 14, Thursday

Sharon took me to hear Barry Goldwater at the Palladium. Just got back. She hates him but wants to see him for herself. Uncle Jules told her to, for practise. She's planning definitely to work for Uncle Jules in Washingtown when she gets out of school in June.

Goldwater said some weirdo things, things that upset Sharon, but made sense to me. Not that he turned me on. Dont get me wrong. He called LBJ haywire & said we havent got a free government any more, but one thats rotting & turning into a police state. Diary, Woody could of told you that 5 years ago & did me. I keep getting surprised at Sharon who thinks peoples votes actually count. If she lived in Watts she'd know better. All the men there get sheets on them down at the precinct, & lose their vote when they go to prison; the wemen control the votes but scared to use them, so you dont have a free government.

Wore my collarless coat, violet side out, & blue velvet hat. Got noticed.

October 17, Sunday

SDS marched down Hollywood Blvd with their groovey clothes (peecock feather hats & indian bells sewed on there cuffs) today against the war but I stayed home & studied, like Dicky promised to do for me. Mean to do well *on my own* this year. So if I dont write much in you, Diary, or put you away entirely, don't be blue. I still love you & will come to you when in need. But if weeks go by, just know I am studing & learning to be a better person & a *more useful* person to whatever cause is right. This time I am taking a full load:

ANTHRO	404	Pre-Literate Social Organazations	(3)
ANTHRO	311	Physical Anthro	(3)
HISTORY	150	Western Civalization	(3)
SOCIOLOGY	150	Man & Society	(3)
ANTHRO	301	Cultural Areas of the World	(3)
			—
			15

As you can see, I am thru with Dance & Rythm (at last!) & have 5 solid subjects. Counting summer school I now have exactly 60 credits so I am a Junior. I am on the honor roll (all A's except a B in Health)!! but Prof Boileau & Sharon still make me stay quiet on account of with all summer in Watts, ect, my talking & writing still somewhat haywire. *I* know that, but after all, 2 yrs. ago I coudent write *anything*, hardly. Prof. Boileau still makes my 3 ANTHRO teachers not count spelling (because he is head of the dept. & can make them), but except for that, *I am on my own.*

ANTHRO 404 is about pre-literate social groups, which I know a lot about since I practicly growed up in 1.

ANTHRO 311 is how peoples bodies are difrent, like the bushmen & the wasps, & like Lily used to talk about, black wemens pelvics being shaped long & narrow instead of round like her (therefore they talk difrent!).

ANTHRO 301 is just about where different tribes live. Its more like geography than Anthro.

HISTORY 150 & SOC. 150 are the courses everybody has to take, no matter what your major, to graduate. They are taught in great big lecture halls & all the tests true/false, ect, so I can pass without spelling good if I just do my lessons. That is why I am taking them now. *Next* year . . . English & Science, that will be the real test. But, if I cant write good next year at age 18 I dont deserve to graduate anyhow.

October 22, Friday

Diary, I once vowed on memory of Mama Pope to keep a record of the Civil War, but things getting so bad I just can't list them all. From now on I will not clutter you up all the time, but will keep a list, to put in you just once in a while, to keep tabs while the unfairness grows. I think this unfairness will go on for years and years, because the Man just isnt going to give in to the poor people, I dont care of its black, mescin or indians. Little childern still getting beat by hunkies, and today more Southern Justice. Some killer named Berkman got let off by a white jury. The prosacuter never even called his witnesses, he was so careless to prosacute. And the final tally on the Watts riots came in today. All 30 or so blacks who got killed by the Man was 'justifiable homocide' (thats how poor Russel is listed); 1 got killed by accident, & 3 criminally. Mama was 1 of them criminally, along with all the 2 whites killed. *In other word*s practicly all the blacks is now okay they are dead. Pardon me for being sour, diary, I know I should lighten up on this, but I been studing hard all week & am very tired. And studing for what? To dye someplace 'justifiably'?

I woud rather think about Dicky.

In his last letter he said, 'you're my girl, I don't care who you know in L.A. I'm saying my beads for you, and when I do Yoga in the mornings I think about you. You're my sister and more than my sister. I'm your brother, and more than your brother. Tell Sharon hello and to think Peace.'

Dicky writes alot. Wants me to come up for Christmas & *I just might.* For once in my life fun to see a white Christmas instead of everybody making do & Rev Smith saying how lucky we are just to be alive. I'd like to see a white & silver tree 12 ft. high & all the bills paid, tons of chocolates, & the air perfumed with rare sent from France. If they ask me, I will go.

I'm wearing a new dress practicly every day. Wore my long sleeved mulberry shift today & could had 4 free cokes from boys but met Andy instead at the caf for lunch. He even goes to class high now.

October 25, Monday

Lary dropped by the lab today. Havent seen him in a 'coons age' as Prof Boileau says sometimes, joking. Alice is dropped out of school & working for some company licking envelopes (or something). He still sees her. He wanted to pay me $15 for a Talal Kozni, on account of LBJ has turned the FBI lose overseas along with the CIA to go after the Commys, & Lary wanted to try & jack off to celabrate. Its an easy $15, why not?

October 26, Tuesday

Same old Lary, as far away from poping his nuts as he ever was, in spite of the FBI, & I woudent let him hurt me, so he dident. Sharon says J. Edgar Hoover comes to del mar racetrack to gambol every year, but no body talks about it.

October 31, Sunday

Flying high.

LBJ says 1 9 6 5 the best year in history. Wonder if Woody knows it yet, rotting in jail in Baltimore. Dicky writes I *have* to come up for Christmas to teach his 'mother some manners', whatever that means. Me teach *her* mannners? He has a groovy new book called 'The Way of Life' and is chinese (but printed in english, of course). About his folks he says from the book, 'men who are stationed high are too fat to dare to die'. I guess Dicky figures people like me & Woody *do* dare to die. Well, thats what he thinks. I hate it, & Woody does too, in secret. Dicky must know that.

November 1, Monday

Went to a meeting with the S.D.S. Turns out they're from all over the place, not just our 1 little gang, kids who groove on politics to stop the war, help the blacks, & take over the universities. Evrybody dressed cruddy in levis and leather coats to show money hasent effected them, & they payed me too much attention. Alot of them smell very bad, Sharon says its their thing to not wash, and theyd rather set on the floor than in a chair, if they have the choice. Well, O.K., but just when I get some decent clothes for the first time I dont want to belong in the SDS & end up dirty setting on the floor.

Now they dont think Lee Ozwald killed Jack, either. If not, who did? I dont even want to think about it being done by somebody else, & have to open up all my old wounds of hate again.

November 3, Wednesday

Diary, there is something missing in my life, now that Mama Pope dead & I dont go to Watts any more. Even the ball is dead, without soul. Am doing good in school, of course, but that takes brains, not soul, & brains only take you so far. Actually, I find school very easy, but, of course I make sure I get all my lessons read. No soul. Dreamed about Dicky last night. He had me in the back seat of his mom's car parked in their big garage, with the door closed & I beating my head on the floor. I yelped so much Sharon come in from her bedroom & shook me awake after it turned into a nightmare. Wrote Dicky & told him about it.

November 9, Wednesday

Glad I'm not back east. They lost all their lights, 30 million people blacked up. Probly fucked like flies when the lights went off. Prof Boileau says the main reason rich people like the Atwaters dont fuck as much as poor like step daddy did, is they leave the lights on more. I didn't know rich people dident fuck as much. I thought they just had more rubbers & pills, but Prof Boileau says, no, they don't fuck as much. I suppose in 9 months there will be a big surge of eastern babys. Prof Pierce who is my Soc. teacher is a real nut on the population explosion. He says we will all be dead in 50 years unless things change. Andy & Ed says the Vietnam war is for keeping boys from fucking & having babys, & to kill them. Woody used to say the war was mostly fought by blacks, & the blacks who werent over there was mostly in prison here & it was all genocide, which means race-killing. You cant fuck in jail or overseas. I dident use to believe him, but do now. & the enamy over there is yellow. Doesn't our leaders know whats going on?

November 12, Friday

Well, Diary, am I embarassed! I'll never write Dicky anything secret again. Mrs Atwater opened my letter to him about my dream in her back seat, & phoned Sharon wanting to know whats coming off? Dicky wrote a letter to me today saying how sorry, 'Damn Mom, she thinks she has to protect Sharon and Augie and me from the whole world. She's always done this with everybody, so don't take it personally. Someday she'll know & love *all* her daughters and know who is brother-sister, and sister-brother. *You* can be a big influence on her, Trixie, but for now you better send your letters with Sharon's. Mom won't open them. Peace and Love.'

Yes, Peace and Love, but Mrs Atwater still blames me.

Diary, a red-letter day. For the first time in history they found a white man gilty of raping a Negro down home. What will he get, 30 days suspended?

November 18, Thursday

I take it back, diary. That rapist boy, Norman Cannon, got *life*. Maybe things *are* changing.

November 25, Thursday

Thanksgiving.

Planned a picnic with the SDS but rained most the week. Everybody to Andys pad in the canals. I did the turkey. All got high, first time for me 'in a coons age'.

Monday was the 2nd Annaversary of Jack – and of you, diary – but for some reason I coudn't write about it, all seemed so far away. Johnson gave a big mushy speech. I feel like he shoudn't have the right to make a speech about Jack. The paper said nearly 12 million seen his grave so far, but not me. If Sharon goes to Washington next year, maybe I can visit her – & Jack's grave. I *do* feel close to him, but don't like the others who are closer, like that stupid woman, who just wrote that stupid book, White house Nanny. Sharon bought it for me, but what a waste of $4.95. No wonder Jackie sore when it came out. That stupid woman said Jack F.K. & Jacky slept in difrent bedrooms. What a lie! They had 4 kids, didn't she know that?

November 28, Sunday

Marched in protest over the war with Sharon & the S.D.S. today, but it was a flop. 600. They had 25,000 in Washington D.C.

December 1, Wednesday

Dicky writes to come up. 'Remember, if *you* come it's *Christmas*, not just another Greedy Day. It's for Jesus. My new book says "He who remains a child, is immune to the vulture's bill." Trixie, *you* are immune to the vulture. Come on up.' Sharon wants me to go, too.

Some lily white named Carol Cota going to be the rose queen this year. Missed it again (ha ha).

December 7, Tuesday

Final report on Watts: 34 dead (which hardly brings back the misery & heartache), 1,032 hurt (including guess-who). 90 cops got hurt, 136 firemen, 10 gardsmen, 23 other from the government & 773 the rest of us.

December 11, Saturday

We are leaving Fri. for Montaray. Cant wait to see Dicky & Augie & walk on the beach. Havent been to Watts all fall.

Sharon got me a drivers learners permit yesterday. That means I can practice on the 17-mile-drive in her MG, if we have time over vacation. Sharon wont get a new MG this Christmas, since a new one in August. She is taking her money instead & giving it to Operation Bootstrap they started down in Watts to help rebild. She thought I would be very happy at this. I am, I guess. I should be, anyhow, but Diary, I am very selfish & would rather she give me the money. I would put it in Savings. You get 4.85% on Savings & it is safe. No telling when I have to move away from Sharon, or Woody might need help. How I would love to spring Woody with *my* money.

Anyhow, she give it to Watts, so that is that.

December 24, Friday

Montaray.

Christmas Eve.

In bed, but wide awake so will bring you up to date.

The Ocean wind blows.

Trixie Mae knows—what?

Augie Atwater has gray eyes.

A little crystal ball and a big one, whose is cracked & whose is true?

One for me & one for you.

Footsteps below.

Outside the pines sing, whoooshshsh and a light from Mrs Hudson's kitchen says: Christmas dinner tomorrow.

I wish I could write poems like I used to, about being hungry when poor Jack was killed. If I was to write a poem now it would be stiff & hard.

POPULATION EXPLOSION
by Trixie Mae Smith

B a a a a m m m m !
Wh a a a ppp!
Zot! Crash!
Here's my kettle
    full of hash!
Here's my hash
    turning hard
Here's a baby
    in the yard.
2 x 2 x 2 x 2
That means: plenty out of you.
2 x 4 x 8
Just too hard to calculate.
Dicky in & Dicky out
    Kettle boiling from his spout

Kettle bubbling on the fire
Population getting higher
Trixie Mae & Dicky Do
Love each other thru & thru
Trixie Mae & Woody, too
Yes they do
Trixie Mae & Andy, too
Lary & Prof. Boileau
Baaammm!
Whaaappp!
Zot! Crash!
Prof. Pierce says worried: No! No! Have done!
But keeps fucking
Because
Its just plain so much fun.

THE END

So here I am, Diary, filling you full of junk because I think I am in the dog house with Sharon – I know I am, with Sharons mother, & embarassed to tell you about it. Me & Dicky took Sharons car driving on the 17-mile-drive which is against the law, because both of us only have learners permits. Well, we had a ball. Dicky was teaching me, & I doing fine till . . . around a curve (this road is nothing but curves, & awful to learn on) – I took it too wide, or something, & run into a car coming the other way. We just barely ticked, but managed to cave Sharons front fender in (including the headlight).

Well, luckily it turned out to be somebody else who lived here. At first, when the woman seen my nappy hair & Dicky so young in old levis, she decided to really mess us up, throw the book at me, & call the cops, but when Dicky told her who he was, she changed her mind & even drove back home to meet Mr. & Mrs. Atwater. Thats what happens when you're rich. She dident even report it. The insurance company will pay but Sharon hasent got a car till next Tues. when we can get it back.

Mrs. Atwater & Sharon really chewed Dicky out for letting me drive. So thats what happened. Dicky & me went down later to the cave & thats when I let him fuck me. He wanted it real bad & since it was *my* fault for wrecking the car, not his, I let him. He was so excited he went off before he was hardly in me. I dont think Augie seen us, but not sure. He come snooping around about 2 seconds after Dicky went off, but if he seen us, pretended he didnt. That was yesterday. We done it again today, but I think we better quit. Dicky even wants to come up in my bedroom, but *thats out*. Its okay for Augie, he's harmless & we can talk about the future & cristal ball & stuff, but not Dicky, he wants to play real ball. I may be his first girl, he's so shy.

Luci Johnson got engaged today. Jackie & her kids is up in Sun Valley. Picture in the paper, cute as buttons. Luci is only 18. I will be 18 next Feb. I wonder who will I marry? Maybe nobody. (If i really want to marry, I shoudent let people fuck me so easy. Make them marry me to get it . . . but then, once they got it, what does that make marrage? Like Dicky's song, Promises Sold By Preachers.) Augie wants to marry me, but I told him for Lord sake never say that in front of his mother.

Mrs. Atwater said Jack F. K.'s sister Pat, who lives in L.A., is getting a divorce from Mr Lawford her husband. I didn't think Cathlics could.

I really like Mr. Atwater. Its Mrs. Atwater who does all the politics. Mr. Atwater said they turned down a hospital for Watts this week up in Sacramento & seemed surprised when I wasn't surprised. I told him it was no surprise, it always happens that way. He said he likes having me around. He said back in N.Y. they sent some black man to the pokey for just *talking* about wrecking the government, let alone doing anything about it, & I told him my best frend was in jail & never done anything bad, that's the way you keep the negroes down, & he seemed surprised that things like that can happen. (I mean Woody) I was surprised he was surprised, but I can understand. Watts doesn't even exist, here on the 17-mile-drive. Even *Woody* dont seem to exist, nor the civil war, out here by the ocean, & if you spent your *whole* time out here like Mr. Atwater, Woody wouldnt exist at all – just the breeze, the birds, the pines & this one road between two far safe gates, guarded at either end from persons who you dont want in.

Won't see Joan Baez. She's out of town.

For Chrismas tomorrow Sharon told me only to get her folks a card saying thank you, but I went out with Dicky to that new hip shop they got in Montaray & found some little round signs of the zodiac baked in clay. Mrs. Atwater is Scorpio, same as Bobby K) & Mrs. Atwater Gemini. They only cost $1, if they dont like them they can throw them away. Anyhow, its something for them to open from me. (I got Dicky a *groovy* metal medalion on a chain called a Onk, or something, made in Egypt supposed to be like the India Tree of Life, I think – wish *I* had it). I got Augie a Weegee Board & I got Sharon a book called *A Guide to Washington D.C.* which I thought was funny since she going there next year. I didnt get Ron or anybody anything this year & cant send anything to Woody.

I cant *start* to tell you what a pretty Christmas tree sparkly silver 2 storys high, & about 500 packages underneath it in the big front hall so when you walk up the curvy stareway to your bedrooms you circle the tree, and on the 2nd story balcony stand tall as its top & look down into *hunderds* of bright ornaments, each one special like a toy horn or camel blown out of silver & glass. They call opening presents 'having the tree' and most the packages were for friends who came to parties just before Christmas, took their presents, & left others for the ones they took, which I guess goes on for days & days. Even Mr. Beeg who runs the house, & Mrs Hudson and the maids get presents (plus extra money on the side, Dicky says) and to hear people stomp & chatter on the stone floor of the hall, with the moist smell of tree through the house, is like movies where stage coaches drive up on snowy nights, everyone shouting God Be With You!

2 a.m. The wind is died down. Santa Claus in the sky for all childern, but rich childern more than poor. I would like to mother all the childern in the world to my breast, I wish I had arms big enough, I would stretch them out like my mama used to, with a shawl, so you got wrapped in her wool wings. I could

hear her heart beat. So would my heart beat for all the child-ern.

God, I love you!

December 29, Wednesday

Been too busy to tell you all that happened, Diary, so you dont know I have a travel case with mirror, brush, & places for bottles of colone ect, all leather & *very* expensive from the Atwaters. Dicky give me a 'The Way Of Life' just like his. We read alot of it on the beach, but we can only understand about ½ of it – also he give me some stamps that come in a roll for writing him, & a box of *groovy* letter paper made like out of old stiff rare paper (he give me these in secret on the beach, so his mom woudent see). Augie give me a model airplane he put together hisself. Everybody laffed but I told him I like it & that He & me can fly away on it. Sharon give me a *very* costly alarm clock for getting up on time (hint, hint) which folds up flat into its leather case. Guess they expect me to do some traveling. Also 6 new albums, including Sounds of Silence (Simon and Garfunkel) just out.

We 'had the tree' in front of the fire laying out on the white bear rug that Uncle Jules killed up in Alaska once & give it to his sister, Mrs. Atwater. Mr. Atwater sat in his favrite leather chair by the fire smoking his pipe & watching me. He is 1 of the richest men in the world.

Walked the beach singing gitar with Dicky & Augie. I havent let Dicky take me back to the cave. We messed around in Mrs. Atwaters back seat for a while in the garage yesterday (like my dream) but too clammy dark & I could tell Dicky felt cheap trying to feel me in his moms car so we went by the fire & played Chinese Checkers instead. Augie can beat both of us at Chinese Checkers, he's so smart.

1966

January 2, Sunday

Dear Diary, well it is a new year. Drove home yesterday. A lovely warm day. I am doing real good in school (A – on my long paper in ANTHRO 301 & expect good grades all around). I am healthy, havent never been sick in 2 years except for colds & cramps. Getting fat and sassy, but still skinny-assed & likely to stay that way. Have good friends, except Woody in jail, but he'll be out this Spring. Have money-in-the-bank (Home Savings & Loan, which Sharon made me open, her daddy has stock there & she says its safe) $364.21, plus whatever intarest at 4.85% I get since Dec. 1. Clothes? *Tons* of clothes, too many to list.

I also got the loan of Sharons record player, got my own transister, & I suppose when Sharon goes to Washington will get the pots & pans & plates & silverware here, tho will offer to buy them used, to show I'm not greedy. Diary, I am not fooling you or trying to. I *am* greedy, be that for good or bad, but you will see I am greedy to do good things which I hope the years prove to be true. And I can have the loan of Sharons car if I can pass my drivers test. I drove down part way on U.S. 101 & I did very good. Fender fixed okay, you cant even see where the wreck was.

So you see, Diary, the year 1 9 6 5 has been very kind to me. Not so kind to poor dead Russel & Mama Pope, and maybe I should never forget that perhaps I profit from the misfortunes of others & should not be so cocky even when things go good.

In the paper today they got a list of most famous people, here is how they line up:

1964	1965
1 – *LBJ*	*LBJ*
2 – Churchill (dead now)	Ike (moved up 1)
3 – Ike	Bobby K (moved up 2)
4 – Rev King	Billy Graham (moved up 3)
5 – Bobby K	Pope Paul (moved up 5)
6 – Gold Water (practically dead)	Rev King (moved down 2) (!)
7 – Billy Graham (cracker)	Nixon
8 – Adlay Stevenson (dead)	Humphreys
9 – Dr. Schwetzer (dead in Africa)	Gold Water (moved down 3)
10 – Pope Paul	Truman

My most famous list is (they got to be alive)

1 – Rev King
2 – Muhammed Ali (Worlds Champion)
3 – Woody
4 – Jacky K.
5 – Bobby K.
6 – Teddy K.
7 – Me
8 – Sharon
9 – Dicky
10 – Augie (or Andy?) (or Prof Boileau?)

My most famous *dead* list is

1 – Jacks memory (martyred)
2 – Malcom X memory (martyred)
3 – Mama Pope memory (martyred)
4 – poor Russel (martyred)
5 – guys like Willy Brewster who got killed & all these years nobody getting punished for it (martyred)

6 – wemen like Mrs Liuzzo, same as #5 but white (martyred)
7 – F. D. Roosafelt
8 – Elenor Roosafelt
9 – My mom (she ought to be higher but I forgot her)
10 – All other fine, dead persons in the world

Well, it is time for vows

1 – keep getting richer & stay in school
2 – help Woody & who Woody wants me to help
3 – *No* more fucking unless *I really* want to, or can get something good for it
4 – Only diddaling before the curse to help get rid of the cramps & at no other time
5 – Not be so bitter, try & be kind & love people more than people do at the college. Recover my soul.
6 – Only take pot when it is embarassing not to
7 – Learn to drive good & *no more wrecks*
8 – quit putting so much *trash* in you, my diary & quit rambeling
9 – Not fuck Dicky again its too dangerous if Mrs. Atwater should find out
10 – Love God, in memory of dear Jack & Mama Pope & the others who are no more except in heaven where they watch over us
11 – Try & plum Mama's crystal ball (but no hopes for 1966 I am so far gone in soul, but how about the years after???) Hope so
12 – Keep my cool at all times especally when it will do me good
13 – try & get over feeling fridays & #13 so creepy, & *have faith in my own strength*

Been reading Dickys present 'The Way Of Life' some. It says in the front, 'The way to do is to be'. Dicky says polatics is ugly & the opposite of Love.

Regan definitely will run for Gov.

I forgot to tell you, on the beach 1 day Dicky said the Atwaters have a place up by Lake Tawho in the mountains thats bilt in a rock where even the H-bomb cant get you. They got it full of food that can last them over a year, & not just crummy stuff, but fancy. Like canned oysters, ect. He says alot of their friends have places there, too, & once when he was 4 yrs old they got a secret call from Uncle Jules the bomb might come & they all rushed up there, but turned out not to be so. Thats the last time he been there. Mr. & Mrs. Atwater dont let their children go, but they got maps, with a key for each kid *just in case*. The valley use to be on roadmaps you get in gas stations, but isent marked on them any more. The rich people had it took off the map to keep it quiet. Hope I'm with 1 of *them* when the bomb happens, & they take me along!

January 17, Monday

Theyre thinking of running Jackie K for New Jersey senator, but I'm sure she won't – at least I hope not.

January 22, Saturday

George Harrison the #4 Beatle got married yesterday in a shaggy fur coat. Groovy. His wife is 5 feet 7, which is tall, a blond model, in a red silk dress. Final exams next week. Andy & Ed wanted to go down to the Hole-a-go-go tonight but I said no. They both groove on Dickys book. Theres a part that says 'leave off learning, going on and on like the sea, drifting nowhere'. Andy clayms thats for him. Well, as Dicky says, thats *his* thing. It isent mine. Been studing all night & am pooped out but want to get all A's if I can. Sharon says I work too hard. I will play when there is time to. Going to have to shorten all my skirts again, but not till after finals. Hems keep going up, & *above* the knees now.

January 28, Friday

Finals over. Hope I did good. Think so. Soc. & History easy, all multaple choice. Wrote very careful in my Anthro courses, but spelling still awful. Sharon knows I keep you, diary, but hasent never asked to see you, which I would not do even if she asked. She said 1 reason my spelling's still bad is *you*, diary. You'd think it would be just the opposite, but she says I keep making the same mistake in you from habit. Andy found out I have a diary, too. He thought for a long time I had a friend who I spent time with, because when I was tired or wanted to write in you, I said 'I have to see a friend' but when he found out it was *you*, he wanted to see. I wouldn't. He says writing in you is like diddaling, all alone with just you & my intermost thoughts. He's just jealous that he doesnt have a diary.

Love you.

February 1, Tuesday

Diary, good news!

I am going on my first plane trip *tomorrow morning* & I am scared petrified! Sharon & me flying up to Montaray for between semesters & has to do with Pat Brown's campain for Gov & maybe me helping down here in Watts with Sharon. Get paid, too, out of the campain fund. Will let you know more when I hear (pray for me in the air tomorrow morning, diary). Plane leaves about 10, so *keep me in mind*! And airborn.

Meanwhile beautiful Jacky K is seeing the Pope, wearing a pretty black coverlet in the paper. She flies all over & dont mind, I shoudent worry about a little trip to Montaray. Mrs. Atwater was right. Jack's sister Pat got a divorce from Peter Lawford. The way you can do that & stay Cathlic is, you cant get married again. It isent the fucking they're against, it's the fucking more than 1 person. I hope Jack dont hold that against me in heaven. People can be good & not be Cathlic, I'm sure his spirit knows that. But I agree, better if I hadent fucked anybody yet, I think. I would like to talk to Jack, who is Cathlic, about this, since I don't feel as bad as I should about it. Maybe they have difrent heavens for Cathlics, but *I hope not*. I want to go where Jack is.

Got a call from Leona this aft. Wanted me to come to hear Julian Bond who got kept off the Georgia legislature at a SNCC rally. Couldent because going north with Sharon. Leona was a little snippy, but who is Julian Bond compared to Gov. Brown?

February 6, Sunday

Made it back. Sunday night. Imagine being up to Montaray, seeing Dicky, playing weegee & crystal ball with Augie & sleeping 4 nights in my big bed up there hearing the rain splash in the gutter, & the wind woooshshing them long-needled pines, to the soft driving roar of the waves against the rocks. Then back here. Diary, flying is like the best dream you could imagine, things so teeny down below like toys. Landed in pouring rain at L.A., really scared, but after the wheels squeak & bounce once, everything safe. Loved it. Spent all week listening to people plan how Gov. Brown can win. Weegee says he will, in the primary. Sharon will stay till Gov. Brown gets elected again, then go back to Uncle Jules in Washington D.C.

Met Uncle Jules, he come in for 1 night & *what a man*, his eyes remind me of Augies, except Uncle Jules is completely grown up. Not very tall, & quite bald, but the second he talks you want to listen forever, it is so clear & understanding & gentle but oh, what power & vision. He has a wife but she dident come, this was a business trip. You could tell how Mrs. Atwater Idealizes her brother Uncle Jules. She is a real ball-buster to her husband when Uncle Jules isn't there, but when he showed up she turned to jelly like the rest of us. Augie is Uncle Jules favrite. Uncle Jules doesnt have any kids except a daughter & wants a son. Augie sat on his lap. Augie keeps his cool, even in front of Uncle Jules, but you can tell how much he likes his Uncle by the way they look at each other, gray-eyes both of them, wide foreheads & strong noses, though Uncle Jules is really well bilt & tough, but Augie always probly a weakling, except in his mind.

All I done was sit & listen, but Uncle Jules nice to me. He has a light in his eye, I can tell, & woudent mind playing around some. It was Mr. Atwater who said I ought to come up (*fly* up! with Sharon, & help down here. Gov. Brown's going to need all the votes he can get. At dinner Mr. Atwater had Augie & me tell about the future in front of Uncle Jules, & when Augie blurted out the bad news 'Regan will beat Gov. Brown in the *finals*!' Mrs Atwater said, 'What?' & then her first mean thing to me: 'What *have* you been telling this child, Trixie Mae?' I could of snuck underneath of the table. I dident tell him anything about who would win in the finals. That kind of wrecked dinner, but the rest of the time good & everybody's cranked up now to get Gov. Brown elected. Dicky & me took a couple walks on the beach & I remembered my vow, but Diary, I am a very weak person & Dicky & me both like it so much I just cant come to believe it is so bad. Anyhow, we done it twice more, once in the cave & once up in the woods. I know I am a fool & am risking all . . . but, sometimes you just plain feel like risking all, & I am *not* a man who can keep his cool like Uncle Jules & Augie.

Augie told me up in my room he was going to marry me again. He's a real caution, & I told him *never* to say that in front of his Mama. Not only that, Augie's got something on Dicky & me now, & its only him whose keeping me out of Mrs. Atwater's dog house again. On Friday afternoon Sharon drove Uncle Jules with Mrs. Atwater to his plane while Mr. Atwater drove Dicky & Augie & me to a movy in Carmel. Don't ask me what the movy was. I never seen it. Mr. Atwater dropped us off but Dicky talked Augie into not blabbing if only *he* went in & we went somewheres else. Augie did it for $5 if we promised to play Chinese Checkers with him that night. Okay. Dicky grabbed my hand & the next thing he'd rented a black motorbike with me on the back & we drove out in the valley back of town. Motorbikes are fun if you can keep your leg off the hot parts & its dry weather, which it was dry when we started.

Carmel valley is 1 of the worlds prettyest places. The road winds past bare orchards which in the summer Dicky says covered with yellow fruit, and the bright red barns & horses & cows snuggle against the green fields rising to high craggy hills on both sides. Thats where Joan Baez lives, Dicky pointed out the house but she always gone someplace making money singing, so doesnt enjoy her house as much as she wants. We turned up a dirt road to a barn where some other motorbikes & foreign cars parked, like Jaguars & Mazeretis (italian). This was *some* barn, all green moss-covered & rotted wood on the outside, but inside a warm cozy room where some hip kids who owned the cars sat around on pillows playing gitars, & 3 or 4 dogs. You could smell grass, but nobody seemed especally high. Dicky hangs out here when he can sneak away from the 'bold marader' (his mother).

Dicky bought a joint off of one of the boys for 1$. 'Politics is nowhere. Who cares who wins?' He slumped beside me. 'I been waiting all winter to show you this place.' He told me the names of the boys & girls he knew & they nodded – none over 17 or so, real teeny boppers, talked so soft nobody could understand who was who.

Diary, Dickys awful turned off of his mother. Once he got in this place he left all his kindness for her & kept saying such wierdo things. He said her politics 'soured the winds & soiled the rivers' (from a song) & as soon as he got 18 he'd come & get me & we'd cut out for parts unknown. Well, I don't *not* like Mrs. Atwater that much. I felt funny there with those zomby rich kids. They dident exactly *watch* me, but you felt underneath their easy laying around their eyes darted sharp looks & remembered things for later. We got a mild high out of the 1 joint & Dicky borrowed a gitar & sang me that Mimi Farina song about the girl with wild & roving wings. Dicky don't hit the cords too good, & has to stop & go back alot, but to hear his gentle voice tell how he weeps when he's left alone & the wind lifts the feathers of the raven, make me think of Woody starving back in some Baltimore jail & I felt very sad. Dickys hand on mine a bird brush, compared to Woody's thrust.

But this isnt what I started. We had to leave to meet Augie so we'd all be there for Mr. Atwater. *But*, on the way back we run into the most terrible rainstorm. In about 2 seconds we soaked clean through & run down our boots, & how the motorbike stayed from drowning out I dont know. So, what to do? Without a word or any big thing, we walked in the *best* store in Carmel where they called Dicky 'Mr Atwater' & ten minutes later walked out with a whole new set of clothes & the wet ones in a plastic sack. He spent $98 & charged it all to his folks! Just like that! We picked up Augie who wanted to know What, right away he seen we had new clothes, but Dicky told him to cool it, & when we got in the car Mr Atwater never noticed. Dicky said the bag had some stuff Sharon asked us to pick up. So that is 1 way to get a new sweater, skirt & shoes! Later we told Augie about renting the bike so he'd keep quiet, but not about the barn in the valley.

So, it is Sun. night, I am listening to my favrite soul singer on KFGJ, you know who Otis Redding, raining hard out, but warm inside (poor Selma-Kitty soaked when we got back – she can get in & out of the kitchen window). Kitty purring between my pretty breasts, & maybe man can do better than what he has. No more riots lately, & a big story from Detroit in the paper how whites is *decent* to blacks back there, & that's why they'll never have a riot like in Watts. That proves there are some good places.

Goodnight, diary. Glad to be home. Tomorrow – Spring term & on to happy days ahead.

February 12, Saturday

18 yrs. old today. Of age. Can do whatever I want that anybody else can, except drink which I dont want to, and vote. Feel the same, but could get married tomorrow & not answering to anybody. Phoned Dicky tonight to wish him happy birthday (he

gets a new car this year, but only a VW, not a sports car till he is 18). Poor Dicky got a cold from the motorbike ride & now is down with Asian flu. Sharon's down too. Its all over the place. She heaved up all last night so my birthday party with the SDS – down at Andys pad called off. Andy has a new bumper sticker, but scared to put it on his car. 'FUCK HATE' The KKK said today it had a plot to kill Rev King & blow up the White House.

Sharons temp is 103 & she practicly delerious. I called her doctor, Dr Fisher, but he said this was normal for flue, to call if it went to 104 or wasn't down by morning. The whole place smells like puke & old bedsheets. Big day at the laundromat tomorrow. So, this is the 18th birthday I been waiting for all my life.

I don't care.

I am happy caring for poor Sharon. She's a darling girl & I love her. I sure miss Woody.

February 28, Monday

Home *sick* in bed.

Now I know what Sharon & Dicky went through. I never been this sick, the heaves, the shakes, the sweats, passed out for hours at a time with fever. Sharon grand. She hardly recovered herself till I come down with it, & this past week been so in-&-out I don't know what's real & what's dreamed. Johnson getting booed wherever he goes, and that awful Lurleen Wallace going to run for Gov. of Alabama, which is all mixed up in my dreams with the first time my step daddy brung home another man for me, I felt this same sick. I closed my eyes so tight I could make my own pictures to blot out that ugly cat on me. Diary, I can never even *hint* these things to Sharon. She woudent like me if she found out. There is a point where nice folks stop caring, if the uglyness gets too bad.

And to top my sick week of fever (except for the loving hand of Sharon & the feely one of Andy, when he comes in) is some man who, it turns out, has a plan to poison every black person in the U. S. of A. by giving out free, poisoned food samples from 4 big centers in the U.S. Oh, dear god, is this my country, or did I dream this, too? Will more get swept into the same assasins abyss as poor Jack? If the crystal ball won't tell me, may God.

March 1, Tuesday

Ah! Woody's out free. Home next week, Leona says!

March 10, Thursday

Seen Woody! Thin & beat after 4 months in 'the Baltimore jail' what a trajedy, to see such a man's eyes clouded & shifty where before so galant & clear, & what a trajedy to see his collarbone so bare of muscle, his ribs stuck out. *But! I found out* the fire burns there still, all he needs is some good cooking to get his strength, and put his mind back on the track. Meanwhile he has strength enough for me. Diary, I'm not good enough for Woody, I know that, but there's more than 1 way to see goodness in the world, I want you to know that, and Woody plaged by all winter in jail & all the misery & shit they threw at him, so if we someday part our ways, remember it isn't all my fault. His mind soft from the slop he refused to eat in jail till he had to go to the hospital from weakness on a stretcher in protestment, but his spirit is here, and only if the famine gets to his spirit, will he cave in. But he is sick as well as well. His brains can't take the hurt of jail & fasting a whole winter like Jesus fasting, without it telling. His voice softer, his eyes dimly not-here, from laying on cold cement floors without anyone to love or care for him like Sharon. Tryed to love & care for him in my way, but our views have changed. Okay, I will take the blame for what happened.

But he still dident have any right to wreck Dicky's book & make me buy another one.

Leona called yesterday that Woody's been back *since Sunday* for some home cooking & to rest up, & decided he wanted to see me after all, when at first he'd said no. So it all begun with his fault, really. Sharon drove me down after class. On a hunch I took The Way Of Life, thought it might help. She didnt go up to Woodys room with me, but drove off. Leona promised to drive me home later.

At first I coudent believe the poor man, was this Woody? lost 20 pounds, mostly off his shoulders, so he looks slumped & skinny like Andy? He made me feel so sorry, but sorry too for that squally room I never noticed before, the ceiling all water-stained orange like somebody wet his pants on it, & the saggy bed enough to break your back, & Woodys blankets smelled like piss. He always so clean before, or did I remember wrong? I guess jail makes you not care. Yes, he needed my help, where never before he needed anything but my body.

'Go ahead, look at Southern Justice,' he told me. Of course I stared at him in shock & hurt surprise, who wouldnt with 20 lbs off his frame, standing by the window in the denims they let him out of jail in, which he refuses to change till everybody sees his misery. Why dident he have on good Afro clothes like Ron wears now? A beautiful Zebra buba or kaftan with a wool belt, & tight pants & sandals?

No.

He has to look like some flappy blue jailbird. Well, that's Woody's thing & it can be beautiful, but I didn't come down to make love to dirty blue denim, there can be beauty even in the mist of honesty, & Woody's pissy-smelling bed & scraggly whiskers just growing back from jail where they made him shave was like some scraggy animal in a dirty cage who's lost his natural ways, not my Woody.

I felt so sorry! And I *never* felt pity for Woody before, only love. I expect too much of that man. I always have. I coudent throw myself in his arms, they looked too weak to hold me. 'Leona says she's fattening you up,' I said.

'She got a ways to go.'

We kissed. I coudent help tears.

He said, like, 'Go ahead, cry, if I'm that much of a mess,' but all I said was he needed his bed changed, & somebody to care.

'I'm at Leona's,' he said, 'I just come here to be alone with you today. I don't sleep here.'

'Just fuck here.'

'Yeah, just fuck here. & you're the first.'

His sickness give him a very bad breath. His skin smelled stale. There isent even a table any more in that terrable room, the curtains so full of dirt they smell like they'd bust into cobwebs if you tryed to move them. So we sat on the bed while he opened my present for him, a cold lobster salad I made special out of chicken stock, fresh cream & mayonase thinking that would help fatten him, and seasoned very light with nutmeg & lemon juice. Sprinkeled with chives. (its one of Dicky's favorites) He ate around the lobster, but said the meat tasted too rich to take, but he ate my hot cornbread. His hand shook. The butter run up his wrist before he finished, & he licked it off. Such skinny wrists, & such crazy talk!

'I've forgot how to eat.'

'Did they treat you that awful?'

'They'd of fed me bean soup, but I didn't eat it.'

'How you fixed for money?'

'Don't pull that shit on me. I don't need your money.'

'It's not mine, it's ours, if you want it.'

'How's Sharon? I hear she got a little brother your hot for. Is he a millionare too?'

'He will be when he's 21.'

'Me too,' Woody said. 'I'm a millionare already. It's in the bank, they just won't let me have it yet.'

'Woody, there's more ways of life than knocking over banks.'

'Name one.'

'There's *love*, Woody.'

'Why, you little cracker.' At least that got him to laughing. 'You fysty little bitch, talking about love. You mean *fuck*?'

'I mean love. True human love, which there isn't enough of.'

'You mean I should go *fuck* the bank, & get the money out that way?'

'Please, Woody.'

'Well, maybe your right, you turned out to be right more than once – at least for yourself.'

'Woody, you better cool it, or I'm leaving.'

'That's what people that *has* money do. After they spend all they want, they take the rest of it out & fuck it once in a while. Then they put it back in the bank.'

I think he's gone off his rocker from being jacked up in jail & too much torment, but he put his hands out – they're still the same soft & strong, though thinner now, & tears poured out of that black man's eyes so fast they dripped off his chin before he could turn his head to hide. Oh Woody. I took you in my arms & felt sobs shake your wasted body, a mans body sobbing out a man heart's misery you had to hide from everybody till you seen me. Lobster salad in the bed. I kissed his wasted cheeks. I told him I loved his hair natural. We kissed, but . . . well, Diary, I wish I could tell you we layed in some nice bed like a bed of dreams someplace up above the world like Monterey, talking about tomorrow on cloud 8, with Coltrane playing sax from below & both of us coming, healthy & good, when we fucked, like the old days. But we couldent, too much changed, & the silence between us too awful, so we had to talk to keep it off our backs.

But talk about what? Woody's misery in jail? That's no way to make him well. My times with the SDS & Dicky? At least I had sense not to bring that up. So we talked about old times, some, Mama Pope chasing the boys away who rattled her fence with sticks, & how good-hearted she always was to the children after all. Woody told me he heard a awful story about Mama once that he doesnt believe (I cant either) where before she come west her mind turned against little children, cause she had a little baby boy about 4 years old out playing with a girl one day, & he pulled her bloomers down like kids do at that age, & a white man seen him do it, caught him, & cut the little boys balls off & left him for dead. 'He dyed later,' Woody said. 'Nobody did anything. Scared to. That's why she walked off from Texas.'

He ate bits of corn bread from the bed. What awful talk! 'Mama never told me any stories like that, she always remembered Texas & her folks kindly. I don't believe it.'

'You believe your step daddy jugged you all those years don't you?' He woudent look up, searching out bits of bread in the blanket.

'Woody, I believe the jail's got to your brain, & if that's all we have to talk about, I might as well split.'

'Okay.'

'The world's full of hate & misery, you know, so long as people like you feed off it. There's another world full of peace & love, if you only pay attention. You don't *have* to smell like piss, you know, you don't have to live in uglyness all your life, just to prove your soul's clean.'

'I guess your right. You ought to know, fresh from all winter with the rich. I'll bet your shit don't even stink any more.'

'It stinks. But that dont mean I have to walk around with it in my pants. And neither do you.'

'That cell I was in, before I went on fast, had anywheres up to a hundred bloods in it, with one open can. Dident even have a seat on it, let alone a lid. I guess I still havent got the smell off me.'

'You have too. But Dicky says . . .'

'Oh? Dicky says?'

'I mean, there's more than 1 way to get justice, you don't have to take to the streets *all* the time. What if justice came in everybody's heart just by *being* good? If everybody *was* good, then you wouldn't need the laws, and the fight'd be over.'

'That's what Dicky says?'

'Lots of people say it, & live it. Rev. King lives it. Sharon's good, you know that. She lives it. You know there's such a thing as a good heart. Jesus had it.'

'Dicky says that, too?'

'Shut up, Woody.' So then, Diary, I made the big fat mistake of showing him Dicky's book.

He quit eating crumbs, or even moving. 'Why, you ignorant little bitch.' But he said it nice. 'You come down here to *educate* me.'

'It's called The Way Of Life. Listen.' So I read the part about being 'utterly humble and you shall hold the foundation to peace.'

'Yeah?'

'Come on, Woody, be serious.'

'Okay. Read me some more.' He layed on the bed & closed his eyes. I knowed he laughed at me in his heart, but at least I tryed. I read for a long time. His face relaxed till he finely fell almost to sleep. His thinned cheeks sunk to his bones. A tired old man. I read a favorite part of Dicky & me (which I will copy here), 'one who has a man's wings and a woman's also is in himself a womb of the world and, being a womb of the world, continuously, endlessly, gives birth. One who, preferring the light, prefers darkness also, is himself an image of the world and, being an image of the world, is continuously, endlessly, the dwelling of creation. . . .' By then Woody fell completely asleep. His mouth opened. He turned his head sideways & snored. I love him. I tip toed to the window. The bloods down on Central stood there doing nothing, just standing around, and the chicks stopped, & talked, & went on, flipping their asses as usal. Woody woke up. 'You stopped reading.' He looked at me very distant. I felt sad & wanted to go home to Sharons.

'You want me to read some more?'

'No. But I'll tell you what you can do.'

He raised up.

'You can take that fucking book and shove it up your skinny ass . . . or, better still . . .' he grabbed The Way Of Life & heaved it out the window – just like that – right through the glass, *crash*!

'Come here, you funky bitch, you ain't leaving till I fuck you right up to your cop-out brain.'

& Diary, he did, as big as ever. But I couldent come, thinking of Dicky's book, cars running over it, & no telling, the cops probly on riot alert already on account of the busted-out window & people looking up below & laughing – ah, he fucked me all right. He dident say any more. He dident need to. He's back.

Then afterwards, I jumped up & cleaned the mayonase & lobster off my skirt & left.

I have a terrable confession to make, Diary. I'm *afraid* down there now.

March 11, Friday

Dear Diary,

Way last fall I started to keep a box score, like I vowed Mama Pope I would, of the Civil War. Well, I kept it, but forgot to put most of it in you, but being with Woody yesterday & feeling so lousy about it made me remember. Yes, Woody, you may of been in jail all winter, but I been keeping score for *history* which may not be the bravest way in the world, but it is *a* way not to forget brothers and sisters ground in the mire.

Collie Leroy Wilkins got found *not* guilty by the whites in 93 minutes for killing Mrs Violet Liuzzo.

Willie Brewster gunned down.

After Collie Leroy got free for killing, they arrested 3 whites for Mrs Liuzzo & only charged them with 'violating her cival rights' though the poor woman lies dead & her husband bereeved, with burning crosses on her lawn. May her name go on the Great Placque.

97 minutes to find those white men not guilty for killing Rev James Reeb last summer.

Many Black Panthers and SNCC workers killed in Ala. – by who? We will never know. One of them, Sammy Younge, tried to use the bathroom in a gas station & for that, shot dead, the killer no doubt to get off in 97 minutes.

Won't let Julian Bond in the Georgia legislature which he should be, he was elected. He works for SNCC & knows Woody.

Found the 3 *black* men who gunned down Malcolm X *guilty* of first degree. Thomas 15 X Johnson, Norman 3 X Butler & Talmadge Hayes. May those 3 misguided creatures pay for their terrible sins through penance & forgiveness & good acts in the name of God & man, and may Whitey stop wounding poor soljers home on leave like that black captain who got gunned down today in Bogalusa. Forgive us all! I could list lots more, but these the main ones. Woody, I will do it *my* way, & you do it *yours.*

March 15, Tuesday

Tonight all over the radio is more riots in Watts. How far will it spread? Woody's out of it, I hope, in his poor shape.

March 16, Wednesday

2 dead in Watts, 25 hurt, but no troops out. Quiet. The cops have a new Code 77, the radio says, to keep rioters from really getting started. But Watts is outside the garrison & the enemy comes from the garrison to stalk amongst us. We are the enemy & we are the loyal. Thats what a civil war is.

June 7, Tuesday

Dear Diary. I just come, in my own hand.

Something is wrong.

I shouldn't have to come in my own hand. I should be filled up by some good man and come because he is in me, coming himself.

But I am all alone. I bet in the U.S. of A. tonight there are 3 or 4 million people like me, diddling & jacking off because they are alone but need to come. ½ of them is wemen. Why can't the men and the wemen meet and fuck and split a couple joints, and then fuck again after a while they've rested, and then go home? Maybe coming twice each, once hard & once gentle?

Why can't lots of things happen? Why can't I be happy? I have just come in my hand. I felt my thing throb when it come – I come – I felt the shivers & the good ooze & wanted all of a sudden to be fucked in every cavity, pumped seed into until I looked like a sunflower, so full of brown seeds around my yellow petals in the warm sun & gentle breeze. I felt the warm sun when I come, juicy hot & tasting acidy but of life like I am sure the sun feels & tastes like when it turns into gentle life. What does that new life acid, DNA, taste and feel like? Can you swallow it like mens scum & have it be healthy for you? Sometimes I want to lean down & lick my own pussy, like dogs do, but can't reach. Does my cherry taste like scum or giss, or DNA? Or like sweet from true & hot sunshine? Does it taste like copper? Or some other kind of shiney metal melted direct from the sun? Does it make sounds when it comes, could you hear it crying 'Joy, Joy!' magnafied when it pulses coming like a teeny prick all inside my covering skin?

Everybody knows so much, but these are things they don't know. They are scared to talk about them. Maybe talking about it wrecks it for them, I don't know. We should all be happy, lie belly to belly, hug like snakes sleep wrapped in each other in winter. Lick sweat. Eat cock & pussy. If we have fleas, pick fleas & eat them like the apes. You don't see apes shooting each other or trying to be governer or presadent, you see them jacking off & picking fleas & cuddling their nursing babies, & many of them live to a ripe old age. They are healthy & hide under trees when it rains. They let their hair grow, and if it is nappy or strait, so what? They sleep together not afraid to touch. They lead me to lie down in soft pastures. They suck the tits of cows at night for milk, and the cows like it. They don't care who is King or Presadent, and share plentiful bananas which dear God, who is in my hand when I come, makes rich on the trees for picking. They are not named Ronald Regan or Gov. Brown or Mrs. Atwater. They are named: 'You' and 'You', and 'You', and 1 of them is named 'me'. They sleep on trees at night, nested in branches, & when the election returns come in, they do not wake up to hear. Even when morning comes they do not hear. They smile at the warming sun, play a while with their dicks, have all the bananas they want, & go around loving the other apes. They are not afraid to put their arms around each other, which Gov. Brown & Ronald Regan will never do to each other. They talk, too, but only say gentle and simple things like, 'Me love you' and 'You stay here, me go get you a banana', or 'this is fun' while they scratch each others thick black hair.

They do not call each other liars, & end up killing & shooting like James Meredith got shot yesterday, his bloody body sprawled, crawling for help across the pavement of a southern road. Today Rev King has taken his place on this road which will never end, because man's road is lined with snipers, who are men, so death and lies and cries of vengance will always be heard. The apes peek out through thick, safe trees watching the men kill each other on the road. Someday they will all be dead from killing each other. Mrs. Atwater has a big gun in her hand because she can't come without a gun to help her. Sharon knows this, but she keeps helping Mrs. Atwater because she is daughter. I help Mrs. Atwater, too. Why? Because I am not happy just coming in my own hand, the hand of God. I want money & clothes & power, & freely say so. I want Woody home to fuck me, & do anything he wants me, to him. He won't stay home unless I got money & power, because Woody is sick for money & power. Woody is walking down man's road, & unless I can be happy merely coming in my own hand, the hand of God, I must follow. The snipers snipe. The road is bloody & scarred black with bombs, but I follow. I know these things.

June 8, Wednesday

Well, Diary, I smoked 2 joints last night alone, & you seen what happened. My mind is not intirely safe, & I know it. Usually I am okay, as you know, and keep headed toward my goals, but last night was election night and too much, all alone after a hard Spring's work at college, & helping Sharon with Gov. Brown's primary campain. He won. So did Regan.

Here it is June 8, 1 9 6 6 & a tug-of-war grips this country between the ugly & bad people, & people like Sharon & Dicky & Woody who are trying each in there ways to make things better – Sharon by her good politics, Dicky 'doing by being' in his young but sweet way, & Woody of course full of blood & soul & anguish on the streets for the right cause. You'd think people like them would win, but they don't. The U.S. of A. headed down the bloody path of sad destruction. When I get high, I see like Andy says he does the horrors of poor America come clear, like (he says) wild eyes of horses froze stiff on the merry-go-round. All spring the lies, deceits, and bloodshed went on, not merely the Viet war killing so many beautiful American bodies black and white that Andy & Ed soon to join unless they can keep beating the draft in school, or acting pretend-queer, or getting a felony bust on grass, or maiming themselves as people do – not only the war, but the vicousness loose which people are harmless against, the terrable beatings give by sergants in the Marine Corps to their recruts; the Hells Angels whipping Black men in Sacramento that Truman's writing poems about; trampeling the state flag of Georgia to shreds (Woody's there); the hunderds of tons of secret guns and grenades and bullets captured in all parts of America by the FBI; the tear gas routing black students from marching on their own campuses, and the cracking down of that boy Sharon & the SDS kids is so high on, Mario Savio and the others at Berkley; the self-burning by ministers braver & wilder by far than faded old Rev. Smith, and bible students burning before the very doors where the Presadents family lives; the fervant marches of hungry Mescin grape pickers to the doors of our capital only to have Gov. Brown resting in Palm Springs when they arrive; the CIA in everything – colleges, unions, and ... the spookiest and most fearsome of all, the *assasination* of darling JFK looks now maybe not Lee Oswald but *somebody else*, and so many people recently dead who had anything to do with those fearsome events as if a wild tiger we thought put to rest is still alive and on his secret and invisable prowl amongst us; Lurleen Wallace, who should not be governer, elected governer of Alabama which is a mockery of all the government and I cannot open my heart to that kind of ugliness, the crooked elections Woody talks about down in Alabama for sheriff; the brutal killing of that poor blood by a cop here in town who was taking his black wife to the hospital with his black baby in her womb, and the cop found not guilty as usual, amidst the ugly hatred of watching blacks whose eyes flash revenge, revenge, and the lootings and beatings in Watts in aftermath. Diary, it does not end. From the bombings of great planes on North Vietnam ordered by our highest leader, to the drawn knives of little children, my ears whine of nothing but civil and general war.

The vision.

So what about me, Trixie Mae Smith, age 18 & healthy & pretty enough? Well fed but still skinny-assed probably forever? Quivering over what I just wrote while under the spell of my vision & cant believe I wrote it. Diary, am I 2 people? One driven by Mama's vision, & the other plain me? Sometimes I think so & am afraid, seeing in the midst of painless plenty while the world seethes, seeing & sometimes not. I pray to God for my saneness & happyness.

I did very good again at college in all my courses. Got A in Anthro 310 which was introduction to anthropology linguistics.

Got A in Anthro 311 which is physical anthropology.

Got A in Anthro 323 which is Prehistoric Cultures, and here is the best part of all:

Got A in Philosophy 150 Main Ideas of Philosophy. But I only got a B in Philosophy 156 Inductive Logic. Prof Boileau had me take the Philosophy because his very good friend Prof. Factor is head of the department & promised to make some allowance for me but as he later said he didnt have to make any allowance for me. In fact, I had Philosophy 150, which I got A, from somebody else, & it was Prof. Factor who give me the B.

I easily understood Inductive Logic, which is when you don't know where you're going but manage to get there just the same. It is different from deductive logic, where you're already there & figure out how you got there. Any how, I did as good as anybody in the class, but Prof. Factor said he couldnt give me an A with a clear conscience since Prof. Boileau made him promise to make allowance for me, and he didnt know if this motive to give me an A was entirely that I deserved it, or partly keeping his promise to Prof. Boileau. That is how philosophers are. They always trying to figure out why they do something, & get so wrapped up in that, that what they do, they do wrong. I think it was dumb for him to give me a B. It's only the second one I ever got. Anyhow, my scholarship is good for this summer and next year so I can graduate.

This summer I will work for Gov. Brown (I am learning to type write) and also take Political Science 150, American Political Institutions; and History 255, the U.S. of A. in the Modern World. They will both be easy, since I been working with the Gov. Brown campaign all I heard for the last 3 months is politics.

So much for school. Sharon graduated last week. She took right off for Monterey. Her dad come down to watch her graduate but her mother too busy. Dicky wanted to come, but his school isnt out, and he has to go to summer school again this year to make up work. Mrs Atwater said they would take his VW away if he didn't. Augie is fine. He skipped a grade he is so smart & will be in the 7th next year though not 11 years old till September. He is way *smarter* in school than Dicky, but Dicky is more generally understanding, I think. Of all the *right* ways – Sharons, Dickys, Woodys – I think Dickys is best. Woody may laugh, but 'the way to do is to be'.

I got 90 credits of college already in the bag & 6 more this summer. If I take 18 next fall & only 12 next spring I will graduate, and *if I keep* my grades up, I will graduate magna cum laude which means, with very high praise. I cant help grinning about it, it is such a big joke. If this was a place like Harvard or Berkeley where you have to take a whole bunch of language & other hard courses, this wouldn't of worked. A college degree.

(I just felt a *terrable* sonic boom shock wave, that rattled the whole apartment. There are some parts about living now that is awful hard on the nerves. Selma-Kitty didn't even seem to notice, I guess she is used to them by now. Cats adjust fast.)

Sharon will be down later this summer. Now she is going to

meetings to find out how Gov. Brown can beat Mr. Regan. I ought to tell her she might as well save her strength, but I am going to get $300 a month for July, August, September, October & November for all my spare time getting votes & explaining Gov. Brown to soul brothers and sisters around here, so why not if they're willing to pay? I seen enough already to know politicians have no fear of spending other persons money (or other persons lives) (or anything) so long as they get elected. Politics is like a disease. Andy says Mrs. Atwater would rather have a caucas than fuck Mr. Atwater. As for me, Woody could fill in the picture: Trixie Mae, gone honky with her rich friends, soft on The Way Of Life, tainted with college & not willing to give a dime's worth to freedom. Leona understands better, & I wish she'd let that stud Woody know it, & not to throw my books out the window. (The window cost him $14, way more than the book was worth (ha-ha)) Leona says Woody's got most his weight back now & he's working with that Stokely Carmical, the new one they got for SNCC who turned down a chance to go to the White House a couple weeks ago on integration. Imagine! Stokely sounds just like Woody. He said integration doesnt count any more, what he wants is political & economic black power. Woody used to call it plain MONEY, but it's the same thing.

June 10, Friday

Passed my drivers permit today!

Andy took me down to the place in his VW. Scared *stiff*, but got a soul brother for a tester so passed with a score of 82 out of 100. You have to get at least 75 to pass. So now I can drive. Sharon left her MG here with the keys, but I won't drive it till she gets back from Monterey. Andy & me come home to celebrate my passing. Got high on 3 joints & a very long fuck for old times sakes. Have enough money in the bank for a used car, but my coin is not going for that, as long as I can use Sharons.

June 24, Friday

Sharon here from Monterey. She is to report to a Mrs. Warshow for work and I will work with Sharon for the campaign. Saw Truman in Watts today. Writing poetry about the Civil War still raging on & showed me some. I am glad somebody is immortalizing the Great Black March through Mississippi where today they turned riot guns on Rev King & drove 2000 with gas out of a school yard where they aimed to camp. Hope Rev King takes care of himself.

June 27, Monday

What a day! Down in Watts for Gov. Brown & had the loan of Sharon's MG, when I got right in the middle of a gang of about 100 cats all after 4 cops, who got beat up pretty bad. Imagine, taking on the Man! Everybody yelling 'Kill Whitey' & it made me actually wet my pants a few dribbles remembering back to the riots when I got winged, but no bullets this time, I guess nobody had a gun. Since I in such a fancy car the cats all thought I was a whore & called me a white man's whore & a disgrace, but I didn't say anything, just sat there till they scattered when reinforcements come & an ambulance. They kicked at the car, but no dents that Sharon could see. (They are just jelous of the car – they thought I was a slick nigger on the hustle & they just wanted what they thought I had.)

I don't think Sharon better go down there any more. Ever since Stokeley's been in the news, & Woody free, Watts is no place for a white, even somebody liberal like Sharon. Even some of the SNCC people quitting, they're so scared of Stokeley. *He means business!*

Had lunch with Truman at Brown headquarters where I got him on part-time for $75 a month for messenger boy.

July 9, Saturday

No school, no work for Gov. Brown. Sharon down at Mrs. Warshow's & me home washing my hair when who should come with some stuff from headquarters for Sharon but Truman! I looked *awful*. He talked me into not processing my hair this time. Maybe he's right. At first, I thought those naturals like Woody & Ron & Leona wear were real freak-outs, 20th C. bushmen, it makes your head look like a black peecock's ass in full bloom.

But now they don't look so bad, & Truman definitely decided to let his grow, too. Kitty on my lap. She's getting fat. Maybe pg. I heard from Prof. Boileau that Lary is busting up with his wife & has bought a motorcycle. I wonder if it's a real one, or just one of those new Hondos. Another 500 rioted in Brooklyn yesterday, but all they did was heave rocks.

P.S. Got only my *second* Kennedy ½ dollar of all time at the laundromat. This one dated 1 9 6 6. People still hording them. I only have 2.

July 16, Saturday

They been rioting all week in Chicago & the Guard moved in today with orders to shoot to kill. The heat does that. *8* nurses killed by a single man, how terrible! I remember feeling scared in the riots, but turned on. Even sexy. Do people screw more in the heat? I wonder. Beds arent as cozy in the heat, but sweat is sexy. Frank Sinatra is 51 & going to marry Mia Farrow who is 21. Justice Douglas who is 67 got married over in the Valley to a girl 23. I feel hopped up tonight. Sharon is out with a bunch of big shot Democrats but I stayed home to study. Watched Man from Uncle & the National College Queen Contest on TV instead (queen contest lily white as usual) but am all hopped up as if I wanted to get fucked, but *spiritually*, not really. I feel the air brittle with cock. Even the old men like Frankie & Mr Justice Douglas feel it, I guess. I feel the angel of death coming down from heaven with a huge hard on. Oh, dear God, listen to the soul of JFK. When I act, I act for him, he is still my guide and our Saviour. Brush of angel wings over me, the air is heavy as the wings beat down, but the angel lifts me up with his cock.

July 20, Wednesday

Sharon come back & found me in a fever Saturday, I must of lost 2 pounds of sweat, the sheets soaked clean through the mattress pad. Been home this week but feel better now, & back to school tomorrow & a big meeting at Brown Headquarters tomorrow night.

I know what happened now. My frenzy last Saturday night came from the Angel of Death striking Chief Parker down. He had just stood up to get a reward at a banquet, when he fell over backwards & died. He was 64. Justice Douglas is 67. The papers been full all week on what a fine man Chief Parker was, but his death has caused a big stir in heaven & drops of sorrow have fell all week in San Francisco & Cleveland & Florida & Chicago & New York, I cant list how many dead & maimed, & how many troops brought out. If Chief Parker hadn't dyed last week he would of this, grieving over all the misery that he *so* wanted to move in & crush. Andy said they ought to say on Parkers gravestone 'Now they're on top & I'm on the bottom,' which goes back to when the Chief got Watts under control last year & said, 'Now we're on top & they're on the bottom,' but Sharon says there's a Roman expression that goes, 'Say Nothing Bad About the Dead, They're Out of It.' I agree with Sharon. Most people do the best they can & love, not hate I think. Truman's scared to come & see me unless he's on an errand. This is a bad part of town for Blacks.

July 31, Sunday

Was invited to a big Demo. dinner with a bunch of big shots but got the curse instead & terrible cramps. Diddled myself but only for the cramps tonight. Felt wonderful, floaty, flying, relaxed. Cramps better but empty inside. If you do it too much you fall in love with your own fingers, the fingers of God, and its not natural to love God except through Him as he shows himself in other people. I would rather get loving any time than get diddled, but when you're flowing you cant exactly invite somebody in. The war rages on. 3000 whites went after a bunch of Chicago marchers today & hurt 60 & burned up 30 cars. I am getting scared to take the MG down to Watts. What if it got burned up while I was driving. Sharon says it costs $3000. Another little riot in Watts, but now the Man got Code 77 in operation it's a lot harder to get anything going than last year, which is probly just as well.

I just felt myself flow out like a gush. My body asking for seed. Sharon can get all the pills we need. She got a man named Warren Somebody down at Brown headquarters who is seeing her, but I doubt if they're making it. Sharon & me still haven't talked about it, she's shy. Having all that money makes it harder for her to love, because she never knows if they're loving because they like her, or fucking the money. In some ways it is good to be poor (but not *too* poor!) because when Andy or Woody come around, it is their cock after my pussy, not their hand after my wallet they are after.

If I was a boy, I wouldn't mind making Sharon, money or not, but I guess her mother figures she better not get knocked up by anybody unless he's important. It's like Jackie K. She still can't turn around but what there's 10 reporters there, & her picture's always on *True Confessions* ect, because her picture still sells more magazines on the cover than any other, Prof. Boileau says. On the other hand, she still fairly young & needs her privacy.

Andy is thinking of burning up his draft card. Dicky Atwater will be here in 3 weeks after his summer school lets out. I suppose he will want to make up for all the times he missed in the cave since last spring.

I feel so depressed from the curse, & the heavy air, I feel actually giddy, as if when the lid of heaven comes down heavy enough like cast iron, your spirit steams out the sides & gets invigorated from the horror of the lid of heaven falling so terribly hard. I hear the zing of death, like quick-flying night-birds of sharp beak, carrying secret messages off, like darts, through the black air. Who carrys the message, Woody? Andy? Dicky? Truman? Lead me to Peace and Salvation!

August 1, Monday

Dear Diary.

Snowed under with homework & meetings, but just want to say for the record, a man sniper killed 15 & hurt 31 more down at the University of Texas. Sharon *very* upset over it. She just set here moaning, 'Texas, Texas, there is something rotten in the state of Texas.' Thats after Hamlet, who said, 'There's something rotten in the State of Denmark' many years ago. He was a prince who they were out to get, like JFK, but he found it out in time.

August 3, Wednesday

Poor Woody. He's about to get in the pokey again, I think. Him & Stokely just *asking* for it down in Atlanta, they nearly had a riot on TV tonight, but I couldn't see Woody, only Stokeley. He is a funny looking guy. Kind of like a real smart rat, but I love that man, such force, such power inside his funny little rat skull, and it looks *so* good to see him wearing overalls, instead of looking like a reverse negative of some hunky businessman or politician. Truman's got asked to read some poems at a Watts Festival they're having in place of last year's riots.

August 6, Saturday

Busy week. Meetings for Brown every night & term paper due Mon. in History, but while my hair is drying, just to tell you they hit Rev King with a rock in Chicago. I would like to heal Rev Kings wounds with my own loving hands, but have to stop now & go to the laundromat, we are *altogether* out of sheets & towels.

August 11, Thursday

Just a quick note, Diary. Finals next week, so I didnt go up north to the State Demo Convention with Sharon, but she sure excited when she left. I think politics turns her on as much as her mother, she could go on indefinitely without fucking or anything else, as long as there's a caucus on. I wonder what Woody did in jail all winter for love? I didn't dare ask him if he had to be a prevert with the others, especally the hunkies, on account of I didn't want to know, but I guess in prison you have to do terrable things or risk beating up or even death by the others & the guards.

August 21, Sunday

Dicky arrives tomorrow, so *must* talk to you, diary, I probly won't have time for a while. Saw Woody last week, that's the main thing I want to tell you about. And *what* a week! Last weekend, before Finals, I had to spend down at the Watts Festival handing out Brown stickers & talking to people. Dee & Betty & Andy & Ed came down to watch the Festival parade, but they agreed with me, Dullsville. The Festival got lots of play on TV, but I can't help feeling like Big Ron & some of his Afro-cots like Ismael Mweusy, (or something like that – they're all changing their names now from their old slave-bit) who say Watts is the same old place, in spite of the frosting for TV. Ismael & Ron right, of course, but at least the reporters go down there now where they didn't use to, and The Times even got off its ass and hired a couple black writers.

The SDS got out of the Festival just in time, because all this la-de-daw ended up in another riot, in spite of all the sweet talk, when about 100 cats including Truman started heaving rocks at some cops, & it took 25 of the Man to cool them off.

The next day Truman gave his reading at the high school to a very nothing crowd, about 75 people where it must seat like 500. Truman just started reading when somebody sat down beside me, & was I surprised. *Woody*. Leona never even knew he was in town. He blew in for meetings to raise money for the national cats during the Festival.

Well, Woody looks his old self, Diary, with only a faintest glaze of famine left in his eye. You'd never notice if you didn't know him before. He's stayed pretty much with denim, but a very good brand, & his black boots nicely polished & smelled good, so he's completely over his jail sickness for this time. He's getting famous now, so people naturally started gawking &, sad to say, took away from Trumans poetry.

So Woody & me left ½ way through to cut down the turmoil. Woody has 2 cats with him now in leather coats that go everywhere he does. He's up in Frisco tonight, but back next week & wants me to get Sharon & Dicky to give him money for the National when he comes back.

August 23, Tuesday

Early morning. Sharon snoring in the other bed & woke me up, Dicky out on the sofa. Should I go out to him? Wouldn't mind, but don't want to make Sharon mad. You ought to see his hair, he's let it go since regular school out in June & it's honey-golden curling to his neck, he looks just like that picture of white Jesus you always see. He has a thin face & a fine nose & those beautiful clear brown eyes!!! that make you want to say 'Yes God I love You' calmly whenever he looks. He's more than beat, he is really hip. Dicky says there are people up in S.F. now who they call Hippies who are real lovely people against war & wanting to follow Jesus or other religions. Dicky wears my big silver medallion that I gave him on a neck thong that's the Onk from Egypt & hasn't had shoes on since he's been here. When I got my drivers permit the book said against the law to drive barefoot, but I guess State Patrol doesn't enforce it for kids like him.

Dicky & me blew some pot Sunday & listened to sides. Beatles, mostly, we got tickets for them next week. Sharon had part of a joint too but now she's seeing so much of Warren Trapp, that square Brown worker so hot for Sharon's (coin? pussy?) she doesn't go around so much with the SDS & thinks I shouldn't either. In fact, SDS turns out to be too far radical left for Sharon, and we're about busted up except for Ed & Andy & Dee & me. Hope Dicky never gets on acid. I never want to see those lovely eyes clouded like poor dead Russel's finely got on cocaine & Stuff, his poor jaundiced eyes bumpy with whites the color of mustard, and black blank pupils as surface as plastic. Not for Dicky.

Dicky just went to the bathroom & Sharon quit snoring. I will cook ham & eggs. They both want to meet Woody very much.

August 25, Thursday

a.m.

Sharon won't leave Dicky & me alone in the apartment, she really knows something up with us. Woody phoned last night from the Hole-a-go-go to meet us today. I told Sharon it might cost them some money but they really want to see him before he leaves for Georgia, & willing to pay. Tuesday at the beach;

no action but lots of talk. Dicky says they will never catch him in a war fighting for the politicians his mother is so dear over, they are all corrupt even his mother. We walked a long time on the beach but people stared so we left. You can't fuck in a VW so we went to Andy's pad for a while & blew some pot but not much. He has a sign that says FUCK COMMUNISM over his matress. I drove the VW home for fun. I like Dicky. He is so fragile. He needs somebody to take care of him & I'm afraid if his mother does it, she will grind him up.

Sharon home when we got back, & a little mad at Dicky for being high because Warren Trapp came over later to meet him. Warren Trapp is a big muscled cornfeeder with horned-rim glasses. All we did was talk about Gov. Brown's chances. Dicky never said a word. Sharon got mad later when Dicky said he didn't care who won, Brown or Reagan.

Warren has a huge Contanental, & is nice to me like somebody is to a maid. He puts his big hand on my rump when Sharon isn't looking, but I cant tell if its dirty or friendly. Time to stop. Off to see Woody.

August 26, Friday

Dear Diary.

Woody's turned his room over the Hole-a-go-go into a collection headquarters with 2 cats guarding the door, a piece of plywood over the bed for a desk, & 3 chairs up from the Hole, but it all looks the same as before. Filthy dirty curtains enough to make you sneeze, the orange water spots all over the ceiling, & where they put the new window on last spring they didn't even bother to wash that gray putty off around the edges where it smeared putting it in. Partly the mess is to look poor, deliberate for simpathy, but I think Woody runs it into the ground.

We drove down in Dicky's VW, it holds him & Sharon & me & Andy okay (*no* joints on him this trip, Woody said to make sure everybody clean in case of a phoney bust) and besides we picked up Truman. That was my idea. I think Truman should meet Woody & get some balls. Woody has *too* much, but there's more in the world than poetry, especally these days.

After we talked polite for a minute, Sharon wanted to know right away what the money she gave would go for, & Woody told her alot about voter signups & paying people to go out in the Miss. countryside (in armored cars, I think) & round up all the voters now the poll tax is ruled out & you don't have to read to vote. Besides that, bootstrap operations, summer camps, 'Anything to cool the heat out of the ghetto, and bring the southern man up to where he belongs.' This soft-talk from Woody I haven't heard since before the riots. He's almost an actor now. He not only has 2 kinds of ideas – the hard & the soft – he's got his 2 ways of saying things as different as night & day. He sounded actally educated, in front of Sharon & Dicky, but I knew the truth – I've heard real talk about how we got the Man by the balls now, & our job to organize anything that comes up so we get the most out of it. Stop the machinery. If a cop comes up & tells you to hand over your piece, ask him if you're under arrest, & if you're not, tell him to get his fucking hands off. That's what Woody really means.

'Tax deductible?' Sharon asked.

'If you make it out to the Leadership Conference.'

So Sharon said she'd think it over for her, & her brother. Gov. Brown needs money, too, & she already give more than her share to that.

Dicky said, 'Why back a losing horse?'

'He hasn't lost yet.'

'Augie & Trixie both know, from the ball.'

Woody said to me, 'You got Mama's crystal ball?'

'She reads it alot,' Andy said.

'It's all cloudy now. The fire wrecked it.'

Woody had Truman raise the plywood off the bed so more could sit down up off the floor. Woody & Sharon sat on the bed. It sagged so they slid together. If it still smells pissy I couldn't smell it, & Sharon's nose didn't wrinkle. She liked it there. Woody gave me a smirk nobody else saw. I know he invited her to the bed just working on her for money. Woody said to

Truman, 'What *you* doing to help besides writing verse, boy?' 'He's in school,' I said. Andy wanted to know what Woody's outfit was doing to stop the draft, & he said like in fun, 'Nothing. The more free training in guns we get on army wages, the bigger *our* army'll be to take over.'

Dicky told him The Way Of Life says the soldier's life is a plague.

'You can say that again,' Andy told him. 'Fuck the army.'

'Shit, boy, it wasn't but 2 or 3 years ago every black man in America would have showed up in a concentration camp if the Man told him to – and he'd of been on time. That's because the Man totted the gun & nobody else did.'

'You're not thinking of *guns* with the money?' Sharon said.

'Of course not. This money's going for voter registration and summer camps.'

'That's what I thought.'

Truman said, 'What happens to a dream deferred?'

'It explodes,' Woody said. 'We all know that.'

Andy got bored & decided to meet us downstairs. The guards at the door let him past when Woody said okay. I felt like walking out too, remembering all the things went on in this room, now people sitting so stiff – why couldn't we just – well, you know, take off our clothes & be free & natural on the beach, instead of all this shit – even trying to write it down like it happened is so *terrably* fake. What *really* happened, Diary, was, Woody needed Sharon's & Dicky's money & would of done about anything to get it. That's why he got Sharon to sit on the bed. I could just as easy sat there. But Woody knows what happens when *skin* cuts through all this other shit, it cuts through, that's what, & on a saggy bed they sat legs together till Sharon nearly tongtied & Andy upset seeing them together, that's why he left. So, let Woody go ahead & pull the skin game with Sharon or anybody else who's got the money. If he thinks that's the way. Now it's late, I'm alone in bed & mad, Dicky & Sharon still in the front room with the TV turned up to cover their talk. I think Dicky wants to give more. Or maybe it's Sharon. I don't like it. Woody shoudent have to make Sharon sit on the bed with him for anybody's money.

August 28, Sunday

You could hardly see the Beatles, so little in Dodger Stadium, & they only played for 1 hour, but Dicky loved them. Later at home we put on Coltrane, I get chills when that man chants A Love Supreme, A Love Supreme, A Love Supreme . . .

September 5, Monday Labor Day

Dicky drove home today, left this morning. We didn't fuck *once* the *whole time* because Sharon here the whole time except when Dicky with her, & then last Wenesday I got the curse so that finished that. Well, maybe for the best. I felt rotten on Fri. & Sat. but we all had a good time at the beach yesterday. Everybody got sun-burned, especially Warren. He's in bed today from it, Sharon says, because not away from headquarters much & pale so the sun really hurts him.

Today after Dicky left, Sharon & me went to the Statler hotel. I will be working very hard for Gov. Brown till school starts, but my heart is not in it. He officially kicked off the final campaign. Funny, I heard from Big Ron that Woody was back kicking off a campaign in Washington with the Black Power people the same day. I got more faith in Black than Brown, in this case. ha-ha I feel good for the campaign, I get my $300 a month & loads of free meals, & what's more, I feel absolutely out of it, & unenvolved. Besides, Warren wants to take me to Santa Barbara or someplace some afternoon in his Contanental. But I wont. It will be bad enough losing the election, without Sharon finding that out about her boyfriend, too.

Diary, I want to say something I find very hard to say with Sharon in the apartment, even though she never asks what I write. It is, that I havent expressed to you this whole time Dicky was here how *passionate* that boy is to me. He is older now, so he kept it under control in front of Sharon, but we spent hours talking talking in his VW or here with Sharon listening in the apartment when we *really* should of been off on that vast & far beach, say, south of Ensenada where we went last year with the SDS naked under the sun and under the moon, loving delightfully or *fiercely* if we wanted, and grooving on each other's mind and soul.

Instead we played a lot of Otis Redding, and Donovan, and Dylan, and Joan Baez and the Mamas and Papas, but with Sharon here & the sides playing it was *not the same* as hearing Dicky's voice alone on the guitar singing the swallow song, the freedom of their flight, but *every place* we went the *whole time* I couldn't touch him like that because somebody would say it was bad. And he felt the same way. Well, he is gone now, & even as I write this to you, my most personal diary, I hear Sharon moving in the bedroom (she's on the phone to sneaky Warren now, or her mom, or somebody) and my soul shrinks. Can I never be with sweet Dicky in a free land under a free sky? Without feeling like a traitor? I hope and pray so.

But, what I really meant to say was, his passion for me grew so vibrant we couldn't stay in the same room without him bursting into radiant smiles (which he couldn't do in front of Sharon) and at dinner it got so we knew *exactly* what the other one was thinking, which made Sharon mad, because her & Warren don't talk that way at all, but instead always polite & just-barely misunderstanding each other all of the time.

I can't write more. With Sharon here I can't release my love and my *knowing* on to this page about Dicky. I sense his presence. He is home now, thinking of me, maybe by moonlight down on the beach by our cave, seeing the dark cave & knowing I think of him. I hope he jacks off & shoots as far as the stars, thinking of being in me all the time. I would like to catch him & cradle him like pearls from a pearly sea. I would like Dicky to knock me up, but mustnt *musnt* ever think of it again, for his sake and for mine.

September 8, Thursday

Big Ron called. Woody got arrested with Stokely & about 70 others in Atlanta. They set bail at $11,000!!! I told Sharon, but she said all her money's tied up with Gov. Brown. I am going to send Ron $100.00. I could send all my money, but then where would I be after Sharon leaves in November? Out flat on my ass. Ron said, no, don't send it all. SNCC has some, too. $100 is so puny. Just the *primary* cost Gov. Brown $500,000, and the *finals* will cost him another million or 2. That is white power. I feel sick when $100 can be so much & so little, like a nightmare where everything keeps changing shape. Being without money in this world is like being born into a bad trip you never get off of. Maybe I shouldn't even send the $100, it won't make that much difference to Woody. Diary, what should I do?

September 10, Saturday

I sent $50, which is the most I ever sent anybody in my life. Sharon & the Gang sent $50, too. That makes $100. I know it is crummy of me, but that is what I did, I hope Woody forgives.

What is time? What is a day? What is conscience, Diary? What is money? I hate money because I never had it & it always meant so much, now I have some, I keep thinking about it & it *infects* me. I am trying to make a confession, Diary, that I am a liar and a cheat. I have not told you the whole truth. I did send a $100 money order to Big Ron so he could send it to Woody. I got over $800 in my saving account & I took $50 out – no, this is where I cant lie to you any more.

I took $25 out.

I got Sharon to give me $25. I got $15 from Andy & $10 each from Ed, Stefanny, Warren Trapp and Dee. That made $105 and here is where I cheated. I only sent $100 to Woody. Why did I do this? It has to do with the money. I don't mind spending coin on *things* & half the time I just spend it & don't even ask how much. (Sharon always asking 'how much' & she has over $1,000,000) But sometimes things come up where you got some money from someplace, & are supposed to send it someplace else, and you cheat. Even your very best friend. This is terrible, Diary, and what I should do is send the left over $5 to Big Ron & also a lot more because the way I sent it, *he* thinks *I* gave the whole $100!

Well, I am in this pickel. I am *not* going to pray to God to forgive me, he knows what I did & has already made up his mind on me. I feel hard against God. Why did God make me work so hard for a few $$$ & let Sharon get $1,000,000 free? How come Woody has to spend his days in jail while other persons walk free who are mean & dirty compared to Woody? I know about the money going into Watts from the government, & how much those Cats feed to the Causes, and lying so that what's for summer camps goes for riot planning, but these lies are basically good. I been lied to all my life about whether I was a beautiful person. I am beautiful but you will never find me winning Miss America because ... *you* know why. So where is God? And that is why my heart turns against Him & I am not going to give Ron any more. How do I know Woody will get it? If that Julian Bond who got elected to the house in Georgia can quit SNCC, why should I give them my money?

I have a terrible stomache ache and feel very upset. The sky is gray and hazy. Heavy. I keep burping little burps & tasting onion from my hamberger at lunch. Yes, I am a dirty & cheaty person who can't be put on trust. My $300 a month from the campaign *I* have cheated on. Many days I haven't done what I should or even showed up at headquarters. They can't check on you, they don't know if you're passing out stickers when you're out, or snuck into a movie. The whole world is like that. It goes back finely to how *you* feel about it.

Big Ron & them others in on the hustle steal *all* the time, but if it's from Whitey or his shit-ass government, it isent stealing, it's getting back just a part of what they owe. And from the Federal government, *anybody* can steal and feel o.k. Over in

Saigon, I read where a big part every day goes to gold in swiss bank accounts from cheaters there.

Oh. What can one person do? Money is a terrible thing! The only reason Sharon doesn't cheat is she doesn't have to. Her great-granpa lied & cheated & killed Chinamen by the hundreds, poor men away from family and hearth like slaves, when he brought the railroads west. But now up at their house on 17-mile-drive you can't smell the blood or taste the lies. Why can't we live without money? Is there no love left when I can cheat poor Woody like this? I am going to take some Pepto-Bizmol which usually helps my stomache. I wonder if people like Gov. Brown & Reagan get stomache aches like this & have to take Pepto-Bizmol to keep their consciences down?

Tonight they gunned down 2 more black boys from a passing car. What if I was to raise my hand against Sharon for her grandpa's sins? I already got the mark of Cain on me. God, if I struck Sharon down, would you strike me down? Would I lay awake with that pure girl's blood on my soul?

September 25, Sunday Night

Dear Diary. I have a few minutes & a little energy left, so I will jot down in you a few things, probably the last entry for some time because school starts tomorrow and I'm signed up for 18 hours. Just came back with Sharon from 2 days in San Diego (terrible smog) talking to a lot of soul brothers and sisters down there about Brown and Reagan. Got a letter from Dicky today. He promised to stay in high school if I would save next summer for him, maybe Mexico. Poor Dicky. He can't remember he's a rich kid & the Man would be on our tails like 20-mule-team Borax, Mrs. Atwater with the whip.

As for the record of the Civil War, the jails in Atlanta are *full* & I can just see Woody having to sweat his time out in puke & crap all over the floor from others, which makes me sick at heart but I have no right to be. (as you know) One note of good news, they reduced Stokely's bail to $1,000 so he is out, but

Woody in because he violated probation on the other bum rap.

The future: college this fall is *real* college, but I ought to do okay. They are mostly freshman courses (which I have put off) & my spelling is better now, even though the science courses will probly mess me up:

BIOLOGY	150	PRINCIPALS	(3)
PHYSICAL SCIENCE	150	PRINCIPALS	(3)
ENGLISH	155	COMPOSITION	(3)
ENGLISH	255	LITERATURE	(3)
SPEECH	155	SPEAKING	(3)
PSYCOLOGY	150	INTRODUCTION	(3)
			—
			18

This is a terrific load, plus doing some secretary work for Prof. Boileau & finishing up the Brown campaign. But I don't have anything else to do & want to keep my mind off my conscience, & *hard work* is the way to do it. Dr. Factor said this was a discovery made by the Puritans & is one of the main ideas behind America. Cover all your sins with sweat.

Poor Kennedys! Bobby's brother-in-law got killed in a plane yesterday up in Idaho. They sure are fated. On the other hand, they breed good.

Diary, I could never kill Sharon for her money. Something from what she said today makes me think *she's* paying my $300 a month for Brown, but they write the checks so it don't show that way. Well, I earned it today, going around telling lies to those poor people my own people. I feel like a prostitute sometimes. (not a whore, a whore *enjoys* what she does)

By the way, Sharon might get me to meet Hubert Humphreys tomorrow night, he's in town. He's the vice-presadent, but they are awful easy to meet before elections, so don't think it's anything too hot, diary, but will let you know if I do. Sharon already met him & says he's a nice man.

September 26, Monday

Met Hubert Humphreys. He has a push-pull, click-click grin which he doesn't really mean, but has to, to get votes. Sharon says not to be so synical, it's all part of the plan to stay in power. If Regan gets in, it will set Calif. back 50 yrs. I don't believe it. I think, about 10 years. Andy wants me to move into his pad in Venice when Sharon goes. Maybe I will, can use his VW & close to school.

October 21, Friday

Been working my poor can off at school & for Gov. Brown, and so haven't had time for you, diary, like I thought I wouldn't. But I have to tell you about today.

I met Bobby Kennedy

I shook his hand.

When I shook his hand I felt myself galvanized right to the pavement like a shock wave going through, even though a very gentle handshake.

I looked at that man, who isn't much bigger than me & looks more wrinkled than I thought, and when I felt that hand in mine, knowing this same hand was once tucked in the womb that carried Jack, I nearly passed out and would of, if the vibrant *lightning* in my backbone & legs hadn't kept me bold upright while Bobby's hand met mine.

Oh, what a thrill. He is just a man, but *what* a man and what secrets he carries with him that I would like to be my secrets, too. *This* Friday was a lucky one. 21 is one of my lucky numbers because it is 3 × 7 & both 3 and 7 are good numbers for me. 13 is very bad because it shows 2 7's should be added up to 14, but one is maimed to 6 in a bad way & wrecks it all. 13 is a *killed & dead* 14, & makes me shutter to think of it. Imagine! Bobby Kennedy!

Bobby landed out at Burbank airport. Sharon & me got very close because Bobby is here for Gov. Brown. He met a bunch of people, talked to the reporters, saw Sharon & I think knew who she was, from Uncle Jules, who Bobby knows real good, & then he looked *right* at me beside Sharon, so wide-eyed and gawky I couldn't move. In the crowd he couldn't see what a skinny little butt I have, & I had on my new yellow jersey v-neck sweater with the white v woven in, & my yellow pleated miniskirt & I think looks very good. (Sharon says I am beautiful & have the prettiest skin she ever seen, people always saying that, and have let my hair go natural which looks better than it used to because a lot of the ads starting to show natural hair – I think finely getting tired of imitating Jacky & her bouffant, that you always had to process) – anyhow, Bobby kept looking at me even while he was supposed to meet in the official party, & that is when Sharon said who I was, and ... the handshake. I owe Sharon alot & she is always very good & kind. But I think Bobby wanted to meet me, irregardless of Sharon being Uncle Jules relative. I hope so. He radiates something powerful. Sharon says he is a Scorpio, & to watch out, but I wouldn't mind getting bit with a bite like his. He isn't Jack, but he is very close. I wish he had a deeper voice, though. His hair is nearly as long as Dickys.

2 weeks till election. Am getting behind at school, & early start for San Bernadino tomorrow to talk over there to some poor soul brothers who I am supposed to flip my ass at & convince Gov. Brown is a good man. He *is* a good man, but what a man has to do to stay in power! It's bound to do things to his heart, no matter how good a heart. He come out with a dumb one the other day. I went with him to an orfanage where a lot of little black girls are, & he told them Ronald Reagan was an actor, & it was an actor killed Presadent Lincoln. Somehow I felt my heart hurt when he said it, as being below the belt. The thing he left in those little girls minds shouldn't be there. But like Sharon says, 'the end justifies the means'. Dicky says the end *is* the means.

I am trying to talk Sharon into us going up to Berkeley next weekend for Black Power Convention. (I am telling her it would get votes, but I really want to meet Stokely if I can & ask him about Woody & what happened. Hope Sharon says o.k.)

October 25, Tuesday

Am snowed with work, getting behind in my classes. Especially Literature, there's so much reading & *hard*. Asked Sharon about going to Berkeley for Brown. She is checking at headquarters tomorrow. Diary, keep your fingers crossed.

October 26, Wednesday

Dear Diary. Sharon says if I am working for Brown I had better not go, because Regan will get too much white backlash votes if Stokely speaks on a state campus, & I should be working to stop Stokely speak, not help, till after election.

October 27, Thursday

Sharon is in her bedroom sore, we just had a big fight & my hands still shaking. She *told* me *not* to go to Berkeley tomorrow to see Stokely.

Diary, I didn't mind so much not going, until she ordered me not to, but that made me mad.

I told her I was *working* for her & her mother & Gov. Brown, but they hadn't bought my whole life.

Diary, Sharon has a streak of her mother in her, I can see. She said, 'When you pledge yourself to work for somebody, you *do* pledge your life in a way. You can't believe in a cause without *believing* in it, & if you *believe* in it, your whole life will be true to that cause, or you are unfaithful & disloyal.'

I told her for $300 a month, I didn't have to believe everything Gov. Brown said, & she said, 'Maybe not, but you have to *act* like you do, & can't do anything to hurt the cause, which is to go hear Stokely.'

I told her there was some things dearer to me than Gov. Brown *or* her mother.

'Or me, too, I suppose!' Sharon said. 'Why did I ever give Woody that $1,000!'

Wow. She just went in & slammed her door. Well, I feel sorry, but I also feel mad. Wow, $1,000. Well, whatever happens, Sharon's leaving for Washington right after election, so we don't have to fight with each other much longer. The rent is paid to the 15th of Nov. She wouldn't even pay it to the first of Dec., so I probly will move in with Andy, at least for a while. Using his car will save $$$, which I must from now on. It took me about 2 yrs. to save $1,000. And she & Dicky gave that much to Woody from just one meeting. Wow.

November 14, Tuesday

Sharon down at headquarters and its good to have her gone. A terribly unsettling night, a raging wind, the hills on fire around town, a 10 brave firefighters dead in the valiant fight, God rest their souls. A likely night to tell you that I have quit the Brown campaign as of last night at midnight, Oct. 31. I went up to Berkeley & Sharon hasn't spoke to me since, except absolutely necessary. She is really pissed off.

Well, I am pissed off too. I have a right to hear Stokely if I want to, Brown or no Brown. Besides, what's one election? Diary, I had a vision once up at Monterey where *everything* comes together at the top no matter how people fight below – Brown, Regan, Goldwater, LBJ, (Bobby even) ect ect ect, and if Sharon thinks one election changes anything, all she is is a victim to the Great Plot that you can't fight, you can only join or die.

And the same goes for Woody & Stokely, my vision said, and while we struggle & fight we are like poor fish in a net who, the more we struggle, get caught tighter while we are pulled in by the Great Fisher upstairs, whoever he may be.

Andy grooves on this, & says acid tells him the same vision as I had up at Monterey, that's why he won't fight, but nobody else grooves on it except maybe Dicky, who says you can't tell the Fisher from the fish.

Yes, I should have said to Sharon, '*you're* trapped too like the rest of us, even if you think your closer to the Great Fisher than me.' But I didn't.

Stayed downtown Oakland, plenty of places to stay, & saw Stokely, all right, with 10,000 others out in Berkeley which I had heard so much about, but didn't get within a hundred yards of him, let alone meet him or ask him about Woody. I didn't even see Ron up there, so not invited anyplace later with any Black Power, but got a ride back to L.A. that night after the talk with a friend of Leona. Hardly worth going up, except to have that many persons who groove together, in one place.

The best part were Stokeley's words. He said there is a greater law than the law of a racist called MacNamara, a greater law than a *fool* (that's what he said) called Rusk, a greater law than a *clown* named Johnson – it is the greater law of *each of us*.

That is Stokely's answer to my vision. My vision sees each of us drawn into the great net of the Great Fisher, but Stokely says, no, the final law is the law of each of us little fish in the wide ocean, even in the net.

He is a great man & wish I would have shook his hand like Bobby's.

Sharon says his talk cost Brown at least 100,000 white backlash votes, coming on the Berkeley campus which Brown has defended all these years, but I think she'll feel better after the election & can go work with Uncle Jules. He is a winner, & one reason Sharon & me been fighting so, is I think she knows Brown is a loser, but can't admit it, even to herself. Well, we will know one week from tonight, & what a joy to have it over, & like Andy says let the next clown take the place of the last to begin *his* circus.

November 4, Friday

Sharon leaves a week from today for Washington. I haven't told you, diary, but I was wrong in getting so mad at her. I promise to make up right after election. I will stay till the 15th then go live with Andy which should be good for both of us. He doesn't know it yet, but one reason I am going is to try & get him off acid. The other reason pure selfish, of course. He says if I live with him he will pay all the rents & ¾ of the food, and I will be able to live on my scholarship & work in the lab, & not cut into savings, which is over $1,000 now. You don't know how good it feels to have that much money. I always could *get* money just by letting guys like Lary or somebody fuck me when I wanted, but now I don't have to, and just have to be nice to people who I want to, like Andy, & not turn any tricks.

November 8, Tuesday Election Night

A soft rain falling. Selma-Kitty came in a minute ago wet with droplets on the tips of her soft gray fur. Now she is licking herself with her rough tongue, one leg stuck straight up & her back curved. I am laying on the sofa studying between looks at TV with the sound off. The returns already in from the East. Lurleen Wallace swept to office in a landslide in Alabama, but Edward Brookes got into the Senate from Mass, the first black man (Ron says he's worse than a hunky liberal & has a white wife). That makes him & Teddy K. as senators from Mass.

Sharon down at Brown headquarters. They have a whole lot of champain there, just in case.

A funny thing happened today in Beverly Hills. Some woman shot & wounded her son because he was headed for Viet Nam & she didn't want him killed – only maimed.

LATER

The Calif. returns has started. Regan ahead.

LATER

Looks like Reagan clobbering Brown. Been studying all night on Psych & Lit, they are my hardest. For some reason Biology & Nat. Sci. is easy. I guess I have a square mind, which is why I got A in Logic last year.

LATER

Poor Sharon. Regan has won & the later it gets the more he's won by. Regan will be on TV in a few minutes, pandemonium rains at Regan headquarters. Brown decided not to come out of his room, but go to bed. I don't blame him. Guess I won't wait up for Sharon, she'll probably blame me for losing, but not by a *million* votes, which is what it looks like.

LATER

Regan on TV. He sure is handsome. I wonder if he will be president. Will talk it over with Augie & the weegee board next time I am up to Monterey – if I am ever up, but may never be again after Sharon leaves.

November 10, Thursday

Sharon leaves tomorrow. The SDS going to have a party for her tomorrow but she didn't want it, so she leaves early in the morning with Warren for Monterey for a few days at home, then to Washington. He is going up to meet her folks. Wonder if it will be those two forever till death do us part? There goes the MG. I had daydreams about her loaning it to me, but only daydreams.

I told her I was sorry I went to hear Stokely, & she said Brown lost so bad it didn't make any difference anyhow. But Sharon is like her mother, she hates to lose, so we haven't rapped much about the election. We decided to make up. I helped her put her hair up, & she gave me a little trim where it grows lower down one side of my neck. She said if I wasn't such a black power chick she'd invite me to Washington, & I said I was through with politics, like Andy & Dicky. Then we had a long talk. She's worried about me living with Andy & said I should go back to the dorms, so I won't drop out. She knows how I feel about acid, she isn't worried about that, but she feels if I get in with Andy I'll get arrested, or something, because I won't have her protection.

So we kissed & made up. Sharon has been very true to me. If anything, Diary, I am the cheaty one with her, & my eyes fill with tears knowing how much love Sharon has given me, & how little I have given back. I am a very hard-hearted creature of God, and God knows it. How I wish the floodgates of all my love and soul *could* open, but I am always crafty where I shouldn't be, instead of loving. God forgive me!

And Diary, take good care of Sharon wherever she may go.

November 13, Sunday

Well, Sharon's fear for me didn't take long to happen!

Sharon left Friday, I got busted Saturday, & now on Sunday have a police record, finger printed, am $100 poorer for bail (which I *hope* to get back!!) and am still only 18 years old, but wiser.

So is Andy.

What happened, was, since we couldn't have a party for Sharon Friday – also to say goodbye to Ed who has to report for the army this week – the 4 of us, Ed & Dee & Andy & me went down to Sunset Strip to just do some lurking & watch the action. The traffic jams there are something else, of course, and we been drinking some beer anyhow (*never* again, I'll stay on pot, rather than beer!) and were all in Andy's VW with the top down & FUCK HATE foolishly pasted on the bumper, hemmed in with cars, & a bunch of teeny-boppers in nutty clothes looking like trick-or-treat ran out on the street, instead of staying on the sidewalk where they belong.

Some Sheriffs chased them, & that's when the turmoil started.

Somebody hit a cop with a rock, so he clubbed some kid on the head, & then a bus that stalled just ahead of us really got it with rocks & bottles, & when the poor scared persons got off the bus, a bunch of teeny-boppers streamed on & busted the windows out. The four of us in Andy's VW mostly watched, but Ed & Dee are so pissed off about him getting drafted, he figured what the hell & went after a cop. That beautiful big Dee hit the cop with a beer bottle & when Andy & me went after them to drag them off, the fools, we all got busted by reinforcements & ended up in jail.

It cost Andy $40 just to get his car back.

When the sergant down at the jail found out stuttering Ed was headed in the Army anyhow this week they let him go, so as not to hurt his record (if you got a record, you know, the army doesn't want you as much). Ed tried to get them to make a sheet on him, but they refused, they said they didn't want to deprive the army of a good soldier the way he went after that cop & good luck in Viet-Nam & shoved him & Dee out the door. So it was Andy and me got it. Andy's got a student deferment which, when they found that out, really freaked them, so they blamed Andy for what Ed did, and of course I got nappy hair, so got booked too.

I wouldn't mind so much (except for the $100) – a whole flock got booked – except it's so silly. I could care less about Sunset Strip. If I get busted, I want it to be for something *good & beautiful*, like Woody, not just freaking out on the Strip. *I am so disgusted*, I told Andy, if living with him going to be like that, forget it, but he's as disgusted as me for getting messed up with the teeny-boppers. We both vowed to stay away from the Strip *from now on.*

So, Diary, here I sit with problems. The apartment bare of everything except the last boxes of dishes & linen and my books. Andy just left with a carload of my clothes & will be back in a few minutes. Kitty-Selma goes with me on the next – & last – trip as I look around at the rooms I remember the many good times we had here, & how – so many months ago – Sharon rescued me from Fat Alice & her dirty mind & body.

Another problem is you, Diary. I don't want to take you to

Andy's. He will read you, even if I say no, and that must not be. If anybody reads you while I am alive they will make smut out of my innermost thoughts that I meant to be clean and honest.

Diary, you need a big locked box. Maybe Prof. Boileau will give me a cubboard at school. You will be safer there. Nothing is safe at Andy's pad on the edge of the slippery Venice canals, & any time fire might strike & I would lose you forever, which would be as bad as sending Jack's soul to hell. No, I will keep you at school, except the tablet I am writing in, which I will keep in my study notes & hope Andy doesn't pry into my BIOLOGY. I hear his car coming now.

November 22, Tuesday

At the library.

Dear Diary. I brought all your tablets to school and can write in you in the library. I told Prof. Boileau I had some private papers to keep in a safe place & he said I could have a whole drawer in his file in his private office, with a key to it. He is a nice man & always has been. His shaking in his hands from some nervous thing (not drinking, he isn't that kind nor pot nor acid, I think) is getting worse but I hope he lives a long time. I can type pretty good now & do some in the lab. I see now what college is. It is *2* things. One is the students that keep filtering through, blossoming & disappearing like Sharon & Lily & all the others I knew 3 years ago. The other thing is the professors who stay on & on. I just can't think of college without Prof. Boileau in his messy old office, painted dark red with Indian masks & Silver Mexican ones on the wall & journals & papers stacked high on every desk & cabinet. He has mementoes all over his desk given him by Native friends all over the world. A walrus carved out of jade from Eskimoes, wood carvings of little naked men from Africa, mother-of-pearl dolls from the Pacific. This is his world, & I just can't *conceive* of the college going on without Prof. Boileau. He didn't really have room in that drawer for my diary, but he made room, and just put all the papers in it on the floor, said he shouldn't of saved them all, anyhow. He wants me to be his secretary when I get good enough. I wonder. If just people like him & me decided, there wouldn't be any Problem at all in the world.

Well, here I am wandering again. Andy & me been doing it every night, of course, & sometimes twice, till I just have to stay at the library to get my homework done. The scareder he gets of the army the more he wants to put it in. Midterms next week & I am going to get alot of C's but so what? I have been working in the Libe from 3 o'clock till 8 & am pooped. Andy meets me at 9, then to Venice, turn on for a little while, maybe walk the mucky canals & then the loving will start again to music. I'll be glad when I get my period. Andy is sure potent for a skinny guy. He wants me to take acid, but I said not before Christmas Vacation, at least. There's too much in the paper about what acid does to your cromosomes, & I want whole babies, someday, not mutilated.

They been rioting all week on Sunset Strip & had to hire 69 new sheriffs. Andy & my trial comes up Friday & I hope we get suspended sentences. I want my $100 back on that bail. The kids at UCLA rioted yesterday because USC got invited to the Rose Bowl. None arrested, of course.

Diary, this is the 3rd anniversary of your birth, and how far we've come together in the memory of JFK who died a martyr 3 years ago today. All day people have flocked to his grave, the radio says. Someday I hope to lay a wreath there too, in love.

November 28, Monday

Dear Diary, Our trial for attacking the cops on Sunset turned out to be a farce. They are still rioting on the Strip every night, so decided to get tough with us who already arrested. They threw the book at about 30 of us all at once, which is called Mass Justice which is not fair and against the constitution, but they do it anyhow. Andy & me both got found guilty, fined

$100, *not* suspended, & 30 days in jail, suspended. I am so mad I could kill that judge who didn't even give us a chance to talk, & so is Andy. But with a 1,000 teeny boppers tearing the Strip apart every night this week, they had to set some examples & we were it. *A hundred dollars*, just for nothing. Well, it is gone, I am poorer & wiser, & they can take the Strip & turn it into a cemetary, for all I care from now on.

November 30, Wednesday

Raining terrible today. I just want to go back to Venice & watch the waves pound in on the beach for a while and pretend their power is my power, & then get a good high & hear them roar in my ears. I feel wild & ready to fly. How long is a woman supposed to stay good & do what other people tell her to? Forever?

December 15, Thursday

Last day of classes before Christmas. Lent Truman $15. He may have to quit school, no coin. His uncle's sick. He could join the army & send money back like all the other cats do, but his eyes too bad I think to join up. Besides, Truman in the Army? Hope he can stay in school. Maybe I will help pay his Spring fees.

1967

January 1, Sunday

Dear Diary,

Alone in the lab. Had planned to stay with Leona & Ron, but the deathlike despair in Watts with nothing fixed since the riots, all the big red heart valentine realty & mark twain realty for-sale signs up & everybody out of work just standing around & junk cars lining the curbs was too much, so I had to get out.

Andy spent New Years with his folks. He couldn't invite me, of course, to his square parents. I heard from Dicky before Christmas. They all flew to Washington for the week with Sharon & Uncle Jules. Just a year ago I was there as a big hero, but heroes are soon forgot, so time for my annual report:

HEALTH: good, though flowing hard today & some cramps in spite of joyous relief last night all alone, with Andy gone. I weigh 109 lbs. & am 5 ft. 3 inches tall, 36-22-30, which will never make me a beauty queen, though I look pretty good now. I used to have those pimples, and fat cheeks like little girls, but am thinner-faced now which, I think, makes my eyes look bigger. Have not been sick for a long time.

MONEY: In the Savings $1,286.23, not counting some interest for Dec. I should have $100 more, but don't. I also have $32.08 in my wallet & will get a check for about $96.00 for lab-work over vacation. Typing cards for Prof. Boileau in International Phonetic Alphabet. I have come a long ways in 3 years.

OTHER THINGS: I have got turned off of clothes lately, I still have tons of stuff from Sharon, but until I go Afro & show up in a Kaftan or buba, happy to wear denims & sweaters & sandals. Being around hippies like Andy & the others down here at Venice turns you off clothes whether you like it or not. I *definitely* am through imatating some middle-class red-legged hunkey chick who think she's got it made.

RESOLUTIONS: none, this year, I just hope I keep on being healthy, keep from getting too up-tight about things, try & be as honest as I can, but keep my cool, too. There is a secret core in me, Diary, which you know all too well: it says, 'I love other people very much but . . . I love myself more.' Something I will have to get over. I am not so selfish as I was 3 years ago, but I have a long ways to go, especially in *soul* which I feel definitely a loss of in college. I need that other flash of soul truth, old Coltrane says A Love Supreme, the world breathes through us so completely but so gently we hardly feel it, the memory of those other lost years, it is our everything. Coltrane says All from God, well, I don't know, it takes a person greater in unselfishness than me to see the Truth which dimly glows in our brains, let alone talk about it. This is what they mean in Psych with the Collective Unconscious. Maybe Dicky can teach me.

HISTORICAL REPORT, US OF A:
1 – False sense of security. Civil War to get *much* worse.
2 – Jackie K. won her big fight to keep certain things out of that new book about Jack that's come out. When the Kennedys get together they are quite hard. They remind me of Mrs. Atwater & Uncle Jules. You have the feeling they would rather have their backs broke than retreat. The suicide rate is up 160% in 6 years amongst the Blacks. That shows that before, the Blacks had nothing worth dying for, but now do. I would never kill myself, I think, at least on purpose. Hope Woody never gets such a terrible idea.

PERSONAL REPORT: I worked very hard over vacation & did not drop any subjects. Still 18 units. Next time I will take 12 units, all Anthropology, to finish my major, work 30 hours a week in the lab for Prof. Boileau, get my B.A. in June, maybe even *magna cum laude*, earn $250 a month, live with Andy, and get some good job from then on for $400 a month or more, marry somebody who will make at least that much, probably way more, have a couple kids, and be on easy street.

Or???

WHAT I WANT FOR THE FUTURE:
—People to love, & who love me.
—To be welcomed into God's heart at all times.
—Woody to *stay* out of jail.
—Me, too.
—A car.
—Money and Power to do Good.
—A couple weeks with Dicky Atwater someplace, without his mother or Sharon bugging us.
—Visit Jack's grave.
—To get some flesh on my rump instead of always having to use a pillow.
—Andy to quit Acid.
—A fair society for everybody.
—Meet Jackie sometime.
—Keep friends with Truman & pray for his great success as a black poet.

TO YOU, DIARY: Three years is a long time. Now you are stored at school. Someday I will take you out and read you and enjoy you, but must ditch you before Andy gets home. Diary, consider my life happy & a success. From now on, I will use you only for emergencies or in dire need of friendship, but 1 9 6 7 looks secure.

February 6, Monday

Dear Diary. We went to S.F. during semester break last week, I thought a change would do Andy good, all he's done lately is lay around the pad listening to Savi Shanker, and threaten to go to India. Well, sometimes I wish he would. Stopped by Monterey on the way home. Mrs. Atwater back east so we had a good talk with Mr. Atwater. He's been wanting to see me ever since last year. We spent the night. Had a walk on the beach with Andy, Augie & Dicky barefoot, but it gets dark so early. I'm worried about Dicky. He's started to let his golden hair grow again in spite of what they say at school, he wants to drop out, he says, 'to move so well his footprint never shows'. (Way of Life). We followed our own footprints back along the beach.

Later Mr. Atwater played some old songs on the organ like Tea for Two. I set by him, pulling stops in & out to change the sounds, & tinkered with the top keys while he played bass. The upstairs hall creaked that night. I imagined all 4 of them, Andy, Dicky, Augie, and even Mr. Atwater, kept wanting to come up to my room for a silent fuck, but kept running into each other in the hall & pretending they were just going to the bathroom instead. Nobody came. I fell asleep dreaming all 4 of them was in my bed, but just lying there, except for Augie, who had his little finger up my ass. It felt cold, like a piece of steel. What a dream!

And when we got back Selma Kitty had disappeared, we're still looking through all the canals for the poor dear.

February 13, Saturday

At the lab.

Dicky called last night to say happy birthday, & that was all, & to say Love & Peace.

Andy stoned, I fixed dinner but he didn't eat it till after I went to sleep. Cold chicken and potato dumplings. I could have slapped the poor boy.

I know now why he's on acid.

He *wants* to get drafted.

He's tired of whoring on his student deferment for old Bomber Johnson, so he's taking one long acid trip till they induct him, and will decide then what to do next. He deliberately being useless to his country. Out on the beach at this very minute, wandering, unless he's fell into a canal. I never know when I get back if he'll be here. Kitty never came back. Tuesday next week is the second anniversary of the martyrdom of Saint Malcolm X and a Black Party will be started in his name to fight Wallace – in the streets if necessary, Leona says. By living with Andy I can save $75 a mo., clear. I decided to pay Truman's fees for Spring. $60 down the tubes.

March 3, Sunday

Well, Diary, Andy got his wish. His deferment cancelled and he reports on March 15 for induction. The poor boy in a state of shock, very pathetic & calm. He hasn't dropped a pill or dragged a joint since he found out yesterday morning. He's in meditation at home while I, in the lab, pray for him and Dicky and all the brave boys, white and dark, who face dying in a war or on the streets. Less than 2 months ago I felt great calm & security. Now Andy, the last of the gang, will be taken away and what will I do? Probably end up in the closet by the lab where I began – or even in the practice room?

Hardly.

Lary is on Sabbatical Leave this year. He's supposed to be off writing music, but Prof. Boileau says he's back east stirring up trouble against Russia. Dicky phoned last night. He wants to quit school. Regan. He was very shocked when he heard Andy has to go. Dicky said Andy ought to tear up his draft card, but that means 5 years in the clink which is too long to waste being a hero, I think.

Truman told me today that new L.A. Chief of Police, Reddin, says when the insurrection starts in earnest (soon), the police won't be able to stop it, and the big companies going have to have their own police force. He said it's time they get their battle plans ready, how to control sit-ins, ect, from inside the plant, & how to keep the Black Power in line. He says you ought to keep 2 sets of books, because the Black Power people go to wreck the books first because they know how that louses up a business (& besides you lose all trace of all the blacks who owe you the scratch); he says to take colored movies, with a sound track, for evidence, & threaten them with citizens arrest; he says build steep roofs so Molotov Cocktails will roll off, and put in roof sprinklers, and take out your big plate glass windows & fill it in with bricks.

This whole thing makes me laugh. All they have to do is give equality, but they won't part with their fucking money. 'The Fire Next Time,' James Baldwin been saying that for many years & now it's *here*!

What great leader will come to guide us through the shambles of our own blindness?

Andy went home to see his folks. They didn't even know he'd quit school. He found out last week for sure that misdemeanors like we got arrested for don't keep you out of the army after all, it has to be a felony. He leaves a week from Wednesday. He doesn't know whether he will serve or go to jail, he will just have to wait and see. Kids all over the country protesting, and Congress wants to draft them all who do. So, where has our free speech gone? Gone to Flowers, Every One, as Dicky sings. I am driving Andy down to the draft center Wed. & he will leave the Vokes here with me till he finds out where he'll be sent. Only 3 months till graduation, I guess I'll keep the pad, I couldn't stand moving back to the lab.

Got my 3rd Kennedy ½ dollar at the grocery today. 1967. Wish people would quit hording them.

March 15, Wednesday

Dear Diary. I am alone. Andy's things are moved out, what little he had. I took him down and he lined up with all those other skinny boys, and herded in a big Greyhound bus & that's the last I saw of him. Ronald Reagan had his first chance yesterday for clemency but turned it down, so some black man received none, and will die in the gas chamber – our first death in many moons, for that is one thing Gov. Brown found it so hard to do, allow another human creature to die in his State. Watched TV in my loneliness tonight. Can't remember what was on. Wish Truman was here with me to read poems of love, not hate, but he's building up traffic violations like all the other cats the cops are out for, & scared to drive. He only writes hate now too. Old Bomber Johnson going to step up the war. I wish Dicky was here to sing on his guitar about loving goodness. I wish it *very* much.

Diary, I sense the worse, with Andy's loss. I am 19 years old, one month, and 3 days, but I feel a hundred. Dicky is 17 years old, one month, and 3 days. Not old enough to vote for a long time, but soon old enough to get fed into the Great Machine. And Truman? 19 with bad eyes, but black & therefore chopped up everyday. All our beating hearts weave invisible spider webs, one across the other. Selma-Kitty still gone. Forever. I hope she is in the lap of a new loved one, or else gratefully dead.

Good night, sweet book.

March 17, Friday

Oh Diary! You poor concluded thing! They're after us – haven't even time to ask your loving help or – whether I should. I am putting you in the drawer with all the rest of you in Prof. Boileau's office and *running off with Dicky* who, whatever else he has, is rich. My god!

YOU MAY NEVER SEE ME AGAIN.

March, 1967

The Los Angeles Times:

> **PERSONALS** Dickie, your mother and father are very worried but we understand. Call collect day or night. Your brother is sick at your absence. We love you. If you need help contact any P.D. in Calif. They have orders to help.

April, 1967

The Los Angeles Times and *Herald-Examiner:*

> INFORMATION WANTED
> Substantial reward for information regarding whereabouts of Caucasian male, 17, 5 ft. 11 inches, blond wavy hair, brown eyes, named Dickie. This boy may be dressed "hip" and may be in the company of a Negro female, age approx. 20, short; light skin and "natural" hair. They may be driving a 1966 VW license OFD-314. Write Box 1821 The Times or Examiner, or call collect from anywhere (715) 343-2212. Very generous reward awaits any lead.

May 1967

The Los Angeles Free Press:

DICKIE
Whatever you've done or whoever you're with we forgive you. Come home, dear. We need you. Your sister grieves for you.

The San Francisco Chronicle:

PERSONALS Large reward awaits information regarding young couple, male caucasian, 17, and female, negroid characteristics, 19, traveling in "Hippie" company. "Dickie" and "Trixie Mae" but may be using assumed names. Well educated, may be on dangerous drugs. Write box 1922, The Chronicle, or call collect day or night (715) 343-2212. All leads generously rewarded.

The Berkeley Barb:

DICKIE
Your brother misses you. Mom asks your forgiveness and Dad understands as always. Please come home, or call. Your uncle is very concerned and so is Sharon.

1968

Dear Diary

I'm putting in you here a Short Story I wrote a while back, telling about last year. It isn't very good because I couldn't put my innermost secrets like I do in you, but hope it tells the story. Anyhow, it is the best I could do & everything in it true.

HOW WE GOT AWAY

During the midst of the Civil War, in the spring of the year 1967 where 3,000 blacks killed or wounded in Detroit & other places that summer, & $100,000,000 in property up in flames, Dicky Atwater and me escaped from the F.B.I., which Mrs. Atwater turned loose because Dicky only 17 and a minor, while I 19, had a black mother, and therefore could contribute to his delinquentcy.

Far be it from the F.B.I.'s or Mrs. Atwater's knowledge that *Dicky* brought his own grass with him when he showed up that night in Venice, and *he* who wanted above all to run off with me and therefore quit High School in his Senior year and came to me, with his beautiful blond hair nearly to his shoulders, his thin sinewy body smooth with young blood, wearing the Tree of Life on a leather thong around his pale neck, and a simple leather shirt and blue denims, barefoot, though still early in March of 1967 and cold.

As soon as Dicky knocked at my pad in Venice, I knew he spelled Bad News. With him here, Mrs. Atwater wouldn't be far behind her avenging angels, the terrible F.B.I. For Dicky wasn't just anybody's Hippie-Saint dropout whose folks don't bother to come looking. His mother has great hopes in politics. Therefore to have Dicky tune in, turn on, and drop out according to

Dr Timothy Leery of acid fame, was much more than a family trajedy in Mrs. Atwater's eyes – a *national* trajedy. Knowing this, my fear came on alot stronger than any pride I felt for him showing up, and though I do love him, told him he had to split – for both our sakes. I'd already been busted once, and was Black, which gives you 2 strikes.

'But I haven't any place to go,' Dicky said.

'Well, come in and get warm. But you got to leave soon. How'd you get here?'

'Sharon's car.'

The thought of having Sharon's midnight blue M.G. here with her bubble top to drive around turned me on, I admit, but that car's so easy to spot and now hot, what good would it do? 'I wish you'd brought your Vokes,' I said. 'Why'd you break your promise to me and not stay in school?'

'Because I love you,' Dicky sobbed.

My heart poured out warm honey when he said it. I remembered all the times we sat together in his VW with the hand brake between, whispering his simple honest beliefs about life, about wanting to run but nowhere to run from all the prejudices forced on us by the world and Mrs. Atwater. In those days we laughed and giggled alot, and then grew serious and full of unsaid passion as yearning softened our glued eyes. Those were happy days. Even those quick times in the cave at Monterey I remembered with great joy because Dicky always said, 'I'm living only for you,' and meant it.

'How long have you been gone, Dicky?' I asked.

'I started down U.S. 101 this morning instead of going to school. They were going to make me cut my hair or expell me. Besides, I've had it. *All* of it. I'm sick of school, sick of this immoral war in Viet Nam, sick of my mother and her immoral politics. I've seen what it's done to Sharon, turning her hard and drawing her to that Warren Trapp who I don't trust. They're engaged, you know.'

His young lower lip quivered. Beneath that lovely hair and mild but determined brown eyes lurked the spirit of a boy who needed a mother's warm, full bosom to cry on, and enfolding arms with a shawl like wings, but whose own mother's milk had been long-curdled by her driving ambitions. We sank to the matress, and as the late afternoon sun sank into the Ocean behind us, Dicky sobbed on my throbbing breast. I felt his warm tears dry on my skin, and the steady beat beat beat of my heart lulled him into sleep after his long 350 mile drive down U.S. 101.

Meanwhile in Monterey Mrs. Atwater probably didn't miss Dicky till dinner time. He usually stayed in town after school (oftener than not at the Barn in Carmel Valley, I bet), because once you were home far out on the 17-mile-drive you were *home*, and that was that. She probably got worried about 5.30 p.m., and probably asked Mr. Atwater to start calling Dicky's friends houses about 6 p.m. By 6.30 p.m. Mr. Atwater probably called the Montrey P.D. & the State Patrol, and they no doubt have a book on the Barn & checked it out, but no Dicky, and by 9 p.m., sick at heart and worried, Mrs. Atwater called her brother Jules in Washington and asked him what to do. One of their first thoughts was kidnapping because they're so rich, and in their heart of hearts they'd find it hard to believe Dicky could leave home on his own, in spite of his hippie views and long hair. So first off they alerted the S.F.P.D. to scour the Haight-Ashbury for Sharon's car and Dicky, where the Hippies had begun to call Home.

I thought all of this while Dick slept against my breast. I thought, too, how nice to nurse the departed spirit of Jack F. K. back to life just like this so Dicky on my breast could metamorphose into J.F.K. and we could have that sweet man once again grace our country & put it right. Idle dreams. We had till about 10 o'clock, I figured, but whether to stay away from the pad, or remain here to answer the phone & tell them I hadn't seen him? In either case Mrs. Atwater wouldn't trust me. The L.A. office of the F.B.I. would get word by midnight. How many people & friends already spotted Sharon's midnight blue M.G. out front and recognized it? Oh, to have his little VW instead, there are so many around and they call so small attention.

Also, what about letting Mrs. Atwater know to relieve her

mind? So by the time Dicky woke up I had a plan. I told him he had to phone his mother from a phone booth and say he was okay so they won't worry about a wreck or kidnappers. Then he had to split from L.A. right away because they can trace calls, and then he had to dump Sharon's car because it's hot. Then hide out someplace till he thought it over, and go back to school. Next week Easter Vacation. He had a whole week to think it over.

'No. I don't want anything more to do with them. I been stifled too long by their love, which is turning into cannibalism.'

'Not your father.'

'Dad's helpless.'

'Then call him, or send him a telegram, but you can't stay here tonight or be seen in the M.G. They probably already got a pick-up on it.'

'There's noplace else. Besides, I want to be with you.'

'No.'

'I'm staying.'

'Then they'll bust *me* too, & the cops already have a sheet on me. What about that secret place up by Tahoe for the H-Bomb that your folks own?'

But Dicky hadn't neither map nor key, and already eight o'clock so in two hours the F.B.I. would show up, so we decided instead (1) for Dicky to park Sharon's car in some nothing place, like off Wilshire back of Bullock's, and (2) phone his folks, then (3) I drive us to the college in Andy's VW, which Andy had left here till he found out where he was being sent after induction. Dicky could then spend the night in the old closet off the Anthro lab where I used to live in the old days and still had all the keys to.

Then I would drive home alone and when the F.B.I. showed up, say I hadn't seen Dicky. This should keep the F.B.I. off our tail for a day or two. After Dicky got his thoughts straight he could drive home to Monterey and tell his mother it was me who got him to phone her so as not to worry her, and she wouldn't hold it against me that Dicky holed up here with my help. I might even be a hero again. (And by all means keep

Watts & people like Truman from mixed up in this, no matter how safe the ghetto might be for hiding, because then all the Blacks'd get slapped with a felony, you can bet on that.)

But those plans didn't work out at all.

The reason they didn't, the F.B.I. moved alot meaner & quicker than we had any idea. Oh, Dicky drove to Wilshire, all right, and left Sharon's car. Then I picked him up to Farmers Market and we had fish and chips. In the hub bub of an open phone booth Dicky called home, which of course an unlisted number which all rich people have. His Daddy answered, but as soon as they found out it was Dicky, his mother got on the phone, meanwhile Dicky heard breathing which very likely somebody else on an extension, taking it all down, maybe the F.B.I.

'Dicky, are you safe?'

'I ran away, I'm all right. Mother, I'm not coming home.'

'Dicky, are you *with* somebody, dear? Where are you?'

'I'm all right. I just . . .'

'Dicky? Who's got you? Where can we come get you?'

'Mother, nobody's "got" me. I just *left home.* Don't try and find me. I'll be all right. Tell Augie and Dad I'm all right. I love you all.'

'Dicky! Darling! Augie wants to speak . . .'

Click. Dicky hung up. He tried to say something but his eyes full of tears.

'Go back home,' I whispered.

Dicky couldn't answer for a long time, but when he could he said he got all choked up not for regret of his mother and family, but because he was mad at himself for not being able to talk without choking up, his mother had such a terrible power over him, and he hated it and was *not* going home. He said she probably wanted to put Augie on just so the call would last long enough to trace while he still talked, and Dicky didn't want Augie to get mixed up in such a trick. So he hung up. 'They'll trace the call anyhow, it's easy to do long distance from a pay phone.'

So, with that in mind, we split from Farmers Market probably only a few steps ahead of the Man.

Thank goodness the college deserted. Friday night. Easter vacation. Even the janitors gone. The matress of old laid rolled in the cupboard. In the midst of our secrecy & fear we felt like brother and sister islands on a foreign sea. We clutched each other for luck. We kissed. We talked about old times, and how Dicky ought to go back to school, and how someday we'd sneak off to Mexico for a long time and live on bananas and fish like the apes, not hurting anybody and far from the evil world so full of cruelty and injustice. Dicky sang a song about leaving the cold of evening & letting the sun rays warm & parch our twisted seeds of doubt. He has a way of moving me into his dream, two minds playing in the same warm, shallow waters of song. In my arms Dicky was able to undo his family ties, and in his I felt the power and safeness of Monterey & got melted to it. Dicky acted shy, so I told him, 'Yes, go ahead.' It didn't take him long, quick like in the cave, needles of young blood surged as Dicky pumped a quick young load into a welcome vessal. Nothing jivey about 17-year-old Dicky, just as there's nothing jivey about Woody, no lovy gush of talk, saying I'm sorry, or high philosophy. Just quick love, in that test of loyalty beyond which nothing works so good in saying, this is It.

Dicky wanted it again and again to make the night last forever, but the flap of the F.B.I.'s avenging wings in my ears told me to leave, and for Dicky to lay low till I came back tomorrow. We nuzzled at the opened door. I felt gone in another sphere. I knew the angels of Death rode Dicky's shoulders down 101, & felt them from his first moment on the porch. I smelled their foul and musty wings over us like the time Chief Parker died, which was why, when I picked Dicky up on Wilshire, I had a paper sack from Venice with Mama Pope's crystal ball, and the last of my diary to take to school for safe keeping. I also had as usual my purse with drivers permit in the wallet, and about $25.00. But not my savings passbook, or the jar of grass hid behind the sugar in the kitchen cupboard. Things I should have took, but didn't think to, in the rush.

I drove home alone. When I turned off Venice Way to the lone entrance into the canals I saw a car in which a lone man sat. He wore the badge of the Angel of Death – the skull and crossbones – jagged across his darkened face shadowed in a streetlight.

The F.B.I.

Horrified, I drove past without slowing down. I circled the canals. At the south exit-only from the canals another car waited on the narrow street. Already they'd spied and ransacked my pad, I knew. With my one arrest, and the jar of marijuana a felony in the cupboard, and already helping Dicky escape, they had me. No choice. I drove on, or face the downward path of unfair ruin already worn so bleak and bare by my sisters. Once the Man starts, you can kiss freedom farewell. Russell. Woody. I drove back to the college.

At first, I thought Dicky'd already cut out, the closet empty & no matress on the floor, but it turned out that he, nervous and afraid, heard my returning key in the lock at this ungodly hour of about 1 a.m., and fearing the worst, dragged himself and matress into the lower cupboard to hide.

'Dicky?'

He pushed open the doors and looked out in relief.

Now it was my turn to cry. I told him about the cops. The phone jangled through the closed doors in Prof. Boileau's office. The Man moved with fearsome speed, driven on by Dicky's worried mother.

'Let's split,' Dicky said. Prof. Boileau's phone wouldn't stop. 'At least we can talk about it in the car.'

'No.' I looked out toward the ocean. Cars slowed on the rim of the campus. He was right. So, with eyes full of fears, confused and nervous, I wrote a final cry in my diary, locked my diary with its other tablets in Prof. Boileau's file, and with only Mama's crystal ball and my purse walked arm in arm with Dicky from the lab, *8 weeks* from graduation but when to return?

For, while at first we just drove to get a place to talk, and then later to look for an all-night out-of-the-way cafe, each mile stretched beyond the last and the first thing we knew, we'd passed Bakersfield, then Fresno, & not too long after daylight we sped out of the Sacramento Valley headed for Haight-Ashbury where we could get lost in the crowds of other hippie refugees who fled the armed camps of society. They'd never expect Dicky to circle back so close to home.

I knew I was running out on Truman and the other souls in Watts, but all I could see was prison on a bust for pot, and Woody's wan face after *his* jail time never left my mind.

(LATER)

How can anybody write about the days and weeks that followed in pointless survival amongst the Hippies, and make any sense out of it? Grass. Acid. Dicky bummed a guitar & sang I want to Run, But there's Nowhere to Run to, into my life you come on electrical sound and flashing light. The Filmore. We rolled & laughed in the moonlight in Golden Gate park. Many of us climbed fences over Japanese gardens, and naked under a waterfall ate wild strawberries growing on a hillside. Dolphins will come and feed from your hand, he sang, as you open your soul to water and land, your soul will color the sky, then searchlights from the Man outside. Laughing and screaming we ran past a tiny temple into tall trees behind and the safe forest of the park. High all day and night. We earned our wasted bread selling *Oracles* and *The Free Press* and *The Berkeley Barb* downtown to tourists, and the Diggers never turned anybody away, always a matress someplace and a joint, Dicky whispered about baskets of air, bottles of life.

After the Diggers, we moved to a house full of Hippies on the park Panhandle whose world through sickly bright rose-colored glasses clouded by a constant high on pot, not to speak of several terrible acid trips which brought back not only the fragmented jewels of Russel & Mama Pope and Sharon's parting smile, but also the dark pearls of guilt for a wasted life suffocated me in a terror of speed faster than the quickest nightmare. I woke in stale sweat and horror, clutching those who stayed to minister to seekers like me their own white truth, and the numb drug dream chilling and hopeless in place of the simple pleasures of fucking, and eating, and sitting in the Golden Gate park hearing the Grateful Dead, the Jefferson

Airplane, and other groups blow your mind before the cheering voices of the free.

Lost weeks in Haight-Ashbury. Andy showed up, head shaved, to get his car back, because he was being shipped up to Washington State where he could use it for at least 4 months more before he went to Viet Nam to get killed. This all in secret, of course, the hawks flew high and low looking for Dicky on the sly, for it was never made public that an heir to the great Atwater fortunes dropped out of sight and probably fled sluttily to Mexico with some black slut whose leanings for magic and leading minors into juvenile deliquentcy cast an evil spell over their blond and confused boy who could do no wrong unless led into it by some evil bitch. For one thing, the publicity would have hurt Uncle Jules who came up for election in '68, and for another, Dicky's mother could not face public defeat.

Dicky kept fairly well off the streets. He box-boyed sometimes in Littleman's Market across from the park. He sold necklaces on commission. He milled with dropouts dressed in old leather coats and tiny purple & orange eye-glasses as they played their barefoot games of acting poor. We met alot of nice people in the incense spring haze, away from headlines, riots and crisis. Actually glad to get away from my Diary, where before I got painful stomache aches from telling such dolerous things as the war in Detroit & riots by dozens & bloody black death down home, I now let heaven blossom through the huge lacy trees of Golden Gate park, wade in the waterfall, let my bare feet toughen on the asphalt and grow soft in grass, bringing yellow flowers and ringing hindu bells and let every day come, each with its own sparkle, like *seen* pearls, and not sullied by Ronald Reagan's turning his neat back on the poor insane in our state, and on the deprived, and the continued killings of old black men in the South and elsewhere despite Rev. King's valiant marches for non-violence.

Lost.

A drop out, afraid to signal for help or even wave friendly, for the search relentlessly on for Dicky and his 'evil partner' under whose magic spell he fell south of the border (so the forces of Mrs. Atwater were probably made to believe).

Luckily, Dicky looks like nearly everybody else – slim, barefoot, Jesusy, clear-eyed, bearded scantily. But alas I look hardly at all like the others, somewhat darker, my nappy hair not loose and Jesusy, but rather in stiff curls, and lips thickened by the natural love and affection of my race. I didn't dress Hippie because safer mingling as a poor, square black girl amongst those black children who hung about the edge of Haight-Ashbury, sometimes talking jivey with pretend love to the Hippies, and then again doing their quick flash of hates blocking doors to Hippie bead shops and not letting tourists in, or picking pockets amongst the crowds of Flower Children, who could always write home for money, but the black children could not.

I felt sad. For one thing, I never thought money really evil. That is, I know it's evil, but I know it's better to have money and risk evil, than to not have it, for without it, good though you may be, you quickly die from disease or starvation or frustration like step daddy & Russel whose black faces became only bones. The Hippies only pretend-poor. When they need, they work at the post office or someplace, they are mostly bright kids who at least finished high school, with a high I.Q., whereas people like poor dead Russel when *he* got hungry & strung out, he stayed *hungry* & strung out, only had about the 2nd grade and couldn't hardly write, in cronic bad health – which is also faced by these black children here & by boys like Truman whose constant dignity is constantly put down. Another thing – and this to me absolutely the ugliest – all my life, evil though it is, whenever I need money I can always turn a trick with somebody like Lary or Prof. Boileau (evil though it is) and get a few quick dollars to tide me over. Not that I'm even close to being a whore, but I was a *poor girl* in Watts, which in desparate straits for those who do not like to suffer or to see those who they love suffer, is the same thing as a whore, you can always go up to Crenshaw where Charleys are cruising for you, if you don't have friends to get it from like Andy to pay the rent. But amongst the Hippies, no market for a body merely for money, because there's too much free loving as it is, and not enough money. When I found out this I felt like a rug I always stood on without even knowing swept from underneath of me – I felt a rock-bottom fear of old poverty terror and it must be how women feel when you get old. I know its a failure of my ever-mean heart, yet all this terror unshared by Dicky who always within a phone call of rescue, though he really tried to fix his life into mine. 'Now that we're here we should just let it happen,' he sang, 'Don't slip away, oh no, don't slip away.' But I steered clear of going out alone with Dicky, for to the private spies, the F.B.I. and the Man, to whom no doubt had been offered a big reward of several thousand dollars, Trixie–Dicky together was a bad scene. So life got cramped in spite of enough food & all the grass & acid. Dicky's vision grew, and just like the draft call sobered Andy off acid, and gave him a peace, so Dicky's finding out that he could really make it in love and work apart from the Atwater fortune & Mrs. Hudson in the kitchen, gave him joy. He knew he could be anything. A great singer, a great painter. Anything, if he was free to roam the streets unfearful of the Man & free from his Mother's Laws. But, of course, he had to cool it till the heat let up, so he slunk lightly under the guise of *'Dicky Smith'*, Hippie, carrying a heavy burden of endness in his heart.

We heard several famous people talk in these weeks. The poetry-saint Allen Ginsberg, a former jew. Allen Watts, who knows about far eastern thought, and of course Timothy Leery whose eyes utterly beyond fathom. And met a very nice and dear man, the Artist-Saint Sanford Cole, who even invited us to his place in the country, and one night Dicky and me got invited to the very fancy pad of the Garsons, who hit it rich with writing that play McBird which is a take off on the killing of JFK. This night, happening in April, I think, shocked me back after a month of highs into the horror of the evils in the world outside, and of a dim but gripping memory of Woody, Stokely, Rev. King, and other heroes of the Civil War which raged beyond the bounds of dreamsville. The crowd, including Dicky and me, went to a nearby pad where things brewed mad and wild. A newspaper clipping hung on a wall, where J. Edgar Hoover called 'McBird' Vulgar, Obscene, Blasfamous, Perverted and a Public Desecration of Every Sacred and Just Symbol. We all read the clipping and razzed Mr. Hoover with our tongues. We talked about this man Clay Shaw just arrested in New Orleans last week for the assassination. We talked like it was the C.I.A. and the F.B.I. that did poor Jack in, instead of a sick & demented man named Lee Oswald who also a communist.

I got sick from it.

Both Dicky and me got stunned back to life by the talk of these awful things, by these persons who are hip, but so active like the SDS in a spooky world that Dicky and I had *delib-ratedly* left behind. These Hip and Active persons have all kinds of plans for how to change the U.S. of A. The Civil War rages here too, and someday in the future, all the rage that showed forth tonight will find its vent in the public air, or in red blood spilling in the streets like so much has already been spilled in the name of civil rights. The terror and thrill of the world outside Dreamsville came back into our veins, we were told to come to San Quentin prison on next Wednesday to march against the death by gas of Aaron Mitchell, whose clemency from Gov. Reagan turned down.

I told Dicky, too dangerous, but even he felt secretly ready for action by now, even risk getting caught. For a month we'd lost ourselves in uneasy peace, protected by hordes of look-alikes from the arrest that awaited us sure as doom, the force that Andy felt before his draft, and all the other brave and confused boys daily feel, and all the men in Watts.

Gov. Reagan's clemency hearing collapsed while poor Aaron Mitchell's mother screamed, 'Lord, lord – why can't you give us a chance like the rest? Why, Jesus, Why?'

But Gov. Reagan did not hear, down in Hollywood for the Oscar Awards, and a helper took Aaron Mitchell's message with a deaf ear.

The next day in his cell poor Aaron tried to keep the Citizens of California from their pleasure by killing himself with his razor. But failed.

So on that fateful morning of April 12, 1967, to be followed by the everdangerous 13th, me, Dicky, and many others drove in friends or strangers cars over the Golden Gate bridge to the gate at San Quentin Prison.

We rode with Sanford Cole, who was in from his country hideaway for the killing. We decorated the arched gate with flowers, and sang 'We Shall Overcome', and 'Saints' and many other songs, hoping against hope when Gov. Reagan heard our voices raised in loving plea, he would relent. But he did not. Aaron Mitchell died, in his 37th Black year, and the sour note of his voice in its parting cry 'I am Jesus Christ!' carried to infect us waiting at the gate as he perished, the first to do so in four years in this state.

A man with the bleak look of Death burst on us carrying a sign 'Gas – the only cure for Black Crime and Red Treason'. I recognised him. He was the George – he really was – whose picture Lary had for years on his piano. I shrank back from that creature, but Dicky and another boy sprang like young lions on him hollering '*We* shall overcome.'

Other cooler heads dragged them off, warning that to attack the Nazi George Lincoln Rockwell with a bloodshot eye (who later got gunned by his own friend) is not the Hippie way. A reverend from a nearby church chanted, and we held hands, swayed in solemn communion, and shared bread and wine that tasted like rubber from a hot-water bottle passed amongst us, while the tortured and deprived spirit of Aaron Mitchell soared to his mother's heaven – or to hell, who knows?

Regan sat in his office a few miles away, tortured by political promises he made in election not to let the living black bodies collect on death row like Gov. Brown had. Mrs. Mitchell cried to Jesus, 'I hope they are satisfied.'

At San Quentin gate, men with narrow ties looked oddly at Dicky and whispered. I felt the terror and thrill of getting caught. My mind confused Aaron Mitchell's death with my own downhill life, the panic struck. A bust for narcotics in L.A., the hate of Mrs. Atwater for Dicky's delinquentcy and everything else she could manage. Woody. The others. Beautiful Dicky not delinquent, but the world which named him so. All these flashed through my head as fear and premonition like the night we split from L.A. made me do not what was sensible but what was right. We went to Sanford Cole's car where our sack lunch was left (and in the sack, Mama's crystal ball now covered in a soft bag and not used these many weeks, but I still carried for special strength and aid).

'I can't go back to the city,' I said, as if the voice came from someplace else.

'Where do you want to go?' Sanford Cole said. He is a lovely man, tall and red-bearded, with big brown poet-eyes and a brain that hears you when you speak, that remembers your name, respects *all things*, respectful of your mistakes, gives you faith that he will protect you, just in case, because he understands. Besides, he's a famous artist and Dicky likes to be with him.

'Not to San Francisco,' I said. 'What happened today made me scared. The same people who hurt Jack Kennedy and Aaron Mitchell are waiting for Dicky and me back in town to kill us.'

Mr. Cole said, 'Dicky, what do you want to do?'

'Trixie's right,' Dicky said. 'She brought her crystal ball this morning. I knew we wouldn't go back, but I don't know where we're headed. Only someplace.'

Sanford said, 'Do your parents know you're all right?'

'Yes,' Dicky lied.

'What about yours, Trixie?' Sanford asked.

'Trixie's parents are dead. Anyhow, she's 19 & on her own,' Dicky told the artist-saint.

'Where do you think you should go?'

'If I have to go back home I'll kill myself,' Dicky said. He meant it, & Sanford Cole could tell.

'To the country,' I said. 'The City – even Haight-Ashbury – is too close to the Evil.'

This statement anguished Sanford Cole I found out later. People are always wanting to come up to his place in the country. He's famous, and people fall in love first with his fame and his red beard, and then with him, because he's generous, doesn't cuss, cares for living things like flowers that other people might grind underfoot, and remembers things you say about yourself. So (as Mr. Cole told me later) he didn't want to help young persons do foolish things against their parents or country, but he wanted to help them *live*, and *come alive*, and in Trixie and Dicky's case he wasn't sure if he should take us on, not knowing for sure who we were & Dicky being so young. However, Sanford Cole was between friends living in the little extra cabin by his house at the lake in the woods, so they could stay there for a few days till their thoughts got straightened out. Besides, he was getting old, and sick of cooking for himself, he told me later, and thought Dicky and Trixie would ease the burden of living alone some. We could cook and chop wood in swap for the food we ate. Besides, we both looked healthy and bright and clear-eyed and Sanford Cole likes healthy persons. He's an Artist-Saint, but he's also hard-headed and sensible like anybody has to be, to make it in this deep sea world, even for a saint.

We three drove north all in his front seat through scattered showers in blustery April to the tall Redwoods instead of back to the noisy and smelly city. Which was a big sacrifice on Sanford Cole's part, because he'd come down the 300 miles not only for the killing, but also for the big Peace March the next Sunday, which none of us walked on, because he kindly followed my superstrong need to flee to the country *right away.*

So we escaped. Nobody got hurt, in spite of the fact the Civil War rolled relentless across the land. Sanford said, 'As long as you're here in the forest for meditation, feel free to do your thing.'

'Trixie likes to write,' Dicky told him.

'Then write a story.'

So I did little by little, and this is it.

We drove to this primevil forest where Sanford Cole lives at the lakeshore with only the owls in the treetops, the fuzzy-eared bobcats fresh from dinners of rabbits. Ringlets of moonlight flicker on the lake, the pines and hemlocks cradle slumbering chipmonks the wind moans in stovepipes the wind sings to my dark, sweet loving heart of legs spread a young head soon in a blood-red sun. 'Bless you. Grow strong,' Sanford Cole said. I whispered, 'God love you.' Brown buck deer peeked deerly out of purple thistles. Oh, big brown eyes like Dicky's big brown eyes. 'Don't hurt me, I only want to nibble,' Dicky said. A white bird dropped a white seed into the dark lake. Seeds of light shone under the black puckered lake skin. 'Mother!' Dicky cried in my sleep. 'There, there, dear.' The brown-eyed buck winked as he pulled his watering pink tongue from the black lake. He padded to his nest.

Pain.

'Dicky, fuck me. I got pains.'

Dicky did.

My pain stayed.

'Dicky, fuck me again.'

'I can't.'

'Then . . .'

'Where, there?'

'Yes, ahhh. I love you. Ahhh . . .' Dicky opened the draft. The stove crackled. Flames shot up, what sounded like chipmonks in the roof only the black stovepipe popping heat 'Ah . . .' Chimney smoke curls into tangled trees. Sanford Cole paints Dicky's face black. We dropped acid. Now . . . into their painting room I dust crusted bottles of blue, orange, yellow, purple, green, this is Dicky's primevil, the towering brush and his blond forelock appears easily back of his easel watching me with the dustmop carefully cleaning their paintings, carefully tickling their easels, thumb through their palatte boards, Dicky watches and waits for the moment, brushes my nose with his fawn beard, daubs on my love mask in white. I with my brush on Dicky's naval circle with purple, painted each other, give him a belly of orange radiant flash to his tits, circle his nipples in scarlet, circle his cock in purple, stripe both his legs like a zebra, chase his spine with vermilion, Sanford laughs like an ape in the forest, wondering why we 3 never brushed up against one another. Brushed up against one another. I took on Sanford's vermilion, aped all the stripes from his Zebra, licked all the purple and puce, rolled him around like a top, doused him in cranberry juice. This is my primevil, the towering blush and the passion rolling first Dicky, and then Sanford, our Host, into white batter, soon to be popped in the oven covered with flour. Can't yo imagine a gingerbread cookie, big as a man with a hardon baked in the lake like an oven? Can't you see the heavens, clear as diamonds, somebody's seed white pearl dropped in the lake of the oven? I caught all their passion full in my white Dolly's teeth. 'Eat what the Lord has provided,' Dicky joyed.

'*You* buryed my dolly!'

'It's over.'

'What?'

'It's all over.'

'You did, *you* buryed her.'

'There there, dear, you must be hungry. You're always hungry after it's over. Good trip?'

'No. Where's Dicky?'

'Down by the lake. He's all right. You're all right, too.'

'My stomach hurts. You did something to me while I was on my trip.'

'Only Dicky,' Sanford Cole said. 'He's your boy. Let's go jump in the lake with Dicky and get this paint off.'

THE END

April 1, 1968, Monday

Dear Diary

Back in Watts, & what a long time away!

I have cleaned everything, including dear you, out of Prof. Boileau's drawers & glad of it. I've put those want-ads in you & my dumb, and the last half absolutely *stoned* Short Story, on account of it tells what happened while I was away from you, but not the real truth like I used to put in you, Diary. The truth is I am going to have a baby in a week or so. That is how my life changed so, when I ran away with Dicky.

Yes, a baby.

His baby.

Moving inside me now & I carried him all these 9 months.

Sanford Cole turned out to be as big a traitor as the rest of them, & turned us in. He thought he did it for everybody's good, so I can't hardly blame that big, red-bearded friend who after all doesn't like jail any better than anybody else, so when Sanford Cole found out who Dicky *really* was, about last September, and still under age, he got scared what the FBI would do & left us there & went to Frisco. He got in touch with Mrs. Atwater unbeknownst to Dicky & me who thought we had a new world born where all the ugly evils of this one left behind. We had our little cabin by the lake all fixed up like a house, with curtains in the windows & screens to keep the chipmonks out, & were going to start a beautiful new race of humans born in love, apart from war & prejudice. We could look out to see ring-necked ducks & blue herons & dark loons on the lake by morning & night, & 'by dawn's early light' gentle white-tailed deer came to drink & frolic with their spotted fawns at the green grassy water's edge, their nuzzles sending circular ripples across the still waters. Dicky cut wood to season for next winter's fires. I planted a garden, but the bunnies ate it. Sanford Cole hates to kill any living things, its against his beliefs, so my radishes & carrots shriveled to nothing. We made up for them by shopping at Safeway supermarket in the village. Dicky grew some grass, but it didn't do as good as it does down here where its hotter, but it worked. We had some good highs with Sanford joining in & once we all turned on, painted each other like savages & we went naked in the woods. Luckily, it washed off in the lake. Squirrels chattered in the mossy trees, harmless snakes sunned themselves on rocks above the lake, we walked among the open, logged-off meadows picking wild huckleberries, and at night bats came to catch tardy insects on whirring unseen wings who seemed only a momentary heavyness in the otherwise tranquil air. Peace. Dicky took painting lessons from Sanford Cole & as the summer turned into fall spent more of his time with him. I didn't care. I sat & thought alot about us, & Woody, & life & what God is like, Sanford always talking about. I decided God is still Good, in spite of Detroit, Chicago, Philly, and now the turmoil Rev. King's having this week in Memphis over the garbage. A black year across the country, as you know, Diary. But we had escaped.

It was just as well that Sanford turned us in. No matter how hard we tried, our friendship didn't take, hid together away from town. Oh, Sanford liked to *see* me, like the time he wove me a crown of wild hollyhock & draped wild lilac over my shoulders, & wanted me to sit on the rock by the lakeshore till the sun went down, looking at my body from all angles & far away. He loved the beauty that he *thought* was me, but not the beauty that was *ME*. I was a danger. He snuck farther & farther back in the woods of his mind. They are nice woods, but I got cabin fever and he knew it. Something had to break.

So in September he snuck off to Monterey & told Mrs. Atwater. At first, she wanted the Man to rope Dicky by the arms & force him in the back of their car to Monterey right then & there & into a military college someplace back east where the teachers have ways of clipping rich kids wings so the wounds don't show. But for once Mr. Atwater stood up, Sanford told us. Mr. Atwater said, no, you will kill Dicky if you force him back like that. Let him stay on till he makes his own mind, even if it takes till Christmas.

'That girl,' is all Mrs. Atwater said (jealous).

So after Sanford got back he had long talks with Dicky away from me, like the talks Dicky & Sharon had about sending money to Woody. I am their friend, but only so far. One day just before Thanksgiving him & Dicky went to the village for groceries & the F.B.I. met them politely in a building. Dicky had cabin fever, too, by then. Homesick, he decided soon to go back to the world. By Christmas (I was 5 mos. along) my nipples started to swell & hips got a little saggy no matter how good I looked elsewhere. We had some long talks about it. We decided we couldn't found a new race after all, in these times. He stayed through Christmas, but by Dec. 27 Sanford drove us both to Frisco. Mr. Atwater met us. We had a little talk in the bus depot & Mr. Atwater asked me how I was. I don't think anybody ever told him how I was, or has to this day, or he would of give me more for Dicky's baby. (He gave me $500 to promise to leave for L.A. & not come back.)

O, Dicky! Did I really love you? Or was I just a big sucker? At first I loved you because you looked like Jesus, & white. Yes, I am color struck & who can't help but be in this unfair country of black slaves? Then I loved you because you were sweet Sharon's brother & we both didn't like the war & the unfair things that went on & decided there *was* a way to live free from the terrible evils of death & slavery & unfairness on all sides. So we tryed to live that way, but if you keep going to Safeway supermarket when the bunnys eat your carrots, instead of killing the bunnies, eating them, & using their fur for clothes & warmth, you can't live away from the evil, you are just playing at it like the Hippies. Killing bunnys is God's way too, you know, which is something Sanford Cole & Dicky can't see.

Then I loved Dicky because he was the only one left to love, hiding in the woods away from the violence & sleeping snuggled every night until he knocked me up, which was not careless on my part, I wanted his baby because this is the way God talks, not out of the woods like Sanford Cole may think, but through pussy & Dicky's lovely young cock.

So for one reason or another I kept loving you, Dicky. You sang beautiful songs about me, like flying in the wind & dancing on green petals. But to think it would take, forever, like 2 trees joined in twisted trunks take, was silly & impossible to dream, for this country. Did you ever have to leave your woman behind? It's not often easy, & not often kind, and the persons to love most dear are Rev. King in Memphis this very minute who lays it on the line in fear & trembling for the downtrod garbage men, not Dicky & Sanford hid up in the woods. I knew that all the time, but the woods so pretty compared to Watts, clean instead of all the junk cars & rotted matresses piled out in back, & these cats pissing against the fence & hollering for you to come on out because all they got is time on their hands.

On Dec. 27 I came back on the bus. It take 8 hours. Woody still has his room over the Hole-a-go-go but he lives in Harlem now and is never here. I got my stuff from Prof. Boileau nice enough to store it from Andy's pad. (The grass all gone, probably stole by the Man. Hope they enjoyed it.) Then I moved down here. Prof. Boileau had my bankbook too. At least they didn't take that. ($1442 plus $59 interest). And I can finish school next fall if I want, he'll give me part-time work.

I've laid in the bed here for many days alone dreaming of

happy times past, listening to the jukebox downstairs & the live sounds at night, & feeling good about my baby. It can't help but be a nice baby. It kicks alot. Mrs. Atwater's first & only grandchild. Leona & Ron aren't having any babies till after the Civil War's over but they're wrong, I think. It will last too long & they will be past it by then.

Diary, it is nice getting back to you. I picked you up from Prof. Boileau months ago but have just let you lay in a kind of dream. Just felt like it today for the first time, maybe because Rev. Kings starting the Civil War again this season in Memphis. Tried the crystal ball a few times. Nothing there except bloody black misery. Scared to look any more.

P.S. There is one other thing which I liked about Dicky, it is his money. Yes, I cannot tell a lie to you, Diary, or even leave one out. If Dicky had just been some lovely but poor boy, I don't think I would of done it. People with that much money surely care about their babies, & now that I am having Dicky's surely he must care. Wonder what Sharon would think – & Warren Trapp, if they knew! I know it's wrong to like money, but I've never got over it.

April 2, Tuesday

Truman – remember Truman? – just left. He's doing fairly good in college, but not as good as I did. Of course, he doesn't have quite as much to offer to people like Lary, ha ha. He still wants to be a poet. His hair's completely natural now, a great big nappy conk. Like it. He still dresses terrible without any style, old maroon shirts all faded out, with the buttons gone, & I don't think he's even shined his shoes. They're so scruffed they look *dead*. His sox still don't have any elastic & his ankles haven't got any thicker, but Truman is smart.

But so pig-headed! They're starting all kinds of programs for Blacks & Mexicans at the college now with government money, & Prof. Boileau says they let twice as many kids in who haven't good grades from high school (4% instead of 2%) so somebody besides athaletes can get in who are dumb like I was 4 yrs ago. But do you think Truman will dress up ethnic in a colored buba & make a good impression? Or wear smooth work clothes like Woody wears & a medallion around his neck? Or a necklace of tiger teeth like Big Ron? So they will *notice* him & give him money?

No.

He looks like he just came out of the Good Will & been walking 20 miles in the dust ever since. Take Dick Gregory, he's running for President, wears groovy boots & work clothes, & is quit smoking till the war's over, says if everybody quit in protest to wreck the tobacco barons, we'd get peace & freedom soon enough. It's somebody like Dick Gregory will end up with all the marbles.

But not Truman. I had to loan him $75 to register for spring term. His uncle's still letting him live there, but he has to earn his school money. He's really out of it.

We had a gas today. I'm off pot till the baby comes, don't want to hurt his circulation, & Truman doesn't smoke it either. He reads me his poetry instead. He writes very good poetry, but hard to understand because he leaves out alot. He wrote one to poor, dead Malcolm X that's short enough to put in called 'Malcolm the Man in the Moon'

Malcolm the Man in the Moon

A cloud across your shining face
cannot keep it
from lighting my black way,
Lovely Malcolm Man in the Moon.

He uses poems to fight off the despair, otherwise he'd be standing around downstairs like those other cats with nothing to do but blow pot & ball the chicks waiting around, till they get knocked up like I am. And for what? For *life*, that's what!

April 3, Wednesday

Leona drove me to County General clinic today. I'm ready to have the baby, the Dr. said. Maybe tomorrow. It's started to settle, & he expects the water to bust. I'm not scared, Diary. I get scared of certain things as you well know, such as when people start to fight, or some cat pulls his piece on you. But I feel very joyous about my baby. I can hardly wait to see him. (Hope its a boy, if not, it will be a lovely girl.) He is upside down inside me right now *thrashing* to get out. My nipples swole with milk. Of course it will hurt me some, but what good thing doesn't? I'm sorry what I said about Sanford Cole. He was only trying to do right, sending us back. I think.

I don't blame Dicky. Maybe in a few years.

Leona will drive me to the hospital, all I have to do is call her. Diary, I am going to have to leave you now, but plan to pick you up with *joy* after I get well & have time. I'll be at Leona & Ron's after the hospital & after that??? All my stuff over there now. Mr. Atwater told me not to call Dicky ever. Wonder if Dicky will ever call me. Someday??? Will he meet his own son side-by-side marching for Right? Will their eyes melt like mine melted to Rev. King's once, & know we understood something deep & special between us? Will my baby someday when he is big help his own unknown daddy from a dark trench to light & safety, in memory to the dead JFK? Or will the daddy lend a helping hand to his unknown son? Diary! I love you and the world so much! I feel the Angel of Death in me now, not down where the gentle baby is, but in my arms & breast & head tingling with communion, seeing Mama Pope (but not seeing clear yet in her crystal ball or will I ever?), seeing dead Russel & the eyes of Mr. Atwater turned away when he gave me the money in an envelope. Can't they know I love them all? Can't they pause where they are, all over the world, & feel the happy hurt of wounded pain in their hearts which opens *love* as a wide gash instead of hate? Can't they? We all walk together in a broad uncovered graveyard, meeting & shunning each other's eyes only to lay together someday soon side by side. The sun will surely rise to warm our bodies into new seeds, My sun rises, kicking & thrashing to get out like a baby giant.

April 4, Thursday noon

The water broke. The baby's coming. This the wonderful day when things start new. *You will hear from me later*, Diary. A New Day. 'I Am A Man!' the black signs say as Rev. Martin Luther King down in Memphis planning to march again tomorrow like he did so bravely last week for civil rights. Meanwhile, a bridge of love joins our hands over the silence, so keep tucked snug, & out of the cold, Diary, & I will do the same. Don't eat too many Baby Ruths & don't get too fat, Diary. I will do the same. But to have a fat baby is something else! Diary, that is a joy you will never feel.

Leona is coming up the stairs.